THE · BUSINESS · SIDE · OF · GENERAL · PRACTICE

Making Sense of General Practice

NORMAN ELLIS

Under Secretary, British Medical Association

Foreword by

IAN BOGLE

*Chairman, General Medical Services Committee,
British Medical Association*

RADCLIFFE MEDICAL PRESS
OXFORD and NEW YORK

A catalogue record for this book is available from the British Library.

ISBN 1 85775 091 8

Typeset by Advance Typesetting Ltd, Oxfordshire
Printed and bound in Great Britain by
Biddles Ltd, Guildford and King's Lynn

Contents

Foreword

A BOOK which explains in clear and concise terms the business side of general practice is long overdue. This book fills the gap. It provides an important reference document for any practice and is particularly relevant to the needs of younger principals, GP trainees and other doctors who have recently entered general practice. Each chapter provides a useful account of a key facet of general practice and tells the reader how to obtain further advice and assistance.

IAN BOGLE
Chairman
General Medical Services Committee
British Medical Association

Contributors

JOHN CHISHOLM, *Joint Deputy Chairman and Negotiator, General Medical Services Committee, British Medical Association*

NORMAN ELLIS, *Under Secretary, British Medical Association*

VALERIE MARTIN, *Accountant, Pannell Kerr Forster*

The Business Side of General Practice

EILEEN FARRANT, *former Chairman, Association of Medical Secretaries, Practice Administrators and Receptionists*

WILLIAM KENT, *Secretary, General Medical Services Committee, British Medical Association*

CLIVE PARR, *General Manager, Hereford & Worcester Family Health Services Authority*

DAVID TAYLOR, *Head of Health Care Quality, Audit Commission*

CHARLES ZUCKERMAN, *Secretary, Birmingham Local Medical Committee; Member, General Medical Services Committee, British Medical Association*

Preface

THIS book is directly relevant to both GPs and their practice staff, particularly to those who have recently entered general practice, such as GP trainees and newly appointed staff.

The book brings together factual accounts of several key aspects of the business side of general practice. My overriding aim has been to describe clearly and concisely the principles and rules governing the business side of general practice. Indeed, a book such as this would have been a most welcome educational aid when I took on responsibility for the general practice division of the British Medical Association (BMA) in 1982; it would have helped to increase my own learning curve as I became involved in the work of the General Medical Services Committee and the Local Medical Committees (LMCs).

There is one area of general practice which is not included, dispensing practice. This important and complex subject cannot be covered satisfactorily in a single chapter. It justifies its own book and this gap in the literature will soon be filled by Radcliffe Medical Press.

The following chapters are based on material drawn from a variety of sources. Chapters 1, 2 and 3 are taken from *Making Sense of the Red Book*, written jointly by Dr John Chisholm and myself. Chapters 12 and 13 on practice accounts and taxation are drawn largely from two analogous chapters written by Valerie Martin, FCA, a partner of Pannell, Kerr and Forster, for *Making Sense of Partnerships* edited jointly by Dr Tony Stanton and myself. The chapter on partnership agreements, which was written by myself, is also taken from *Making Sense of Partnerships*.

The task of writing this book has been particularly challenging. I have been faced with the discipline of summarizing, in a single chapter, the principles, rules and basic facts relating to a specific key area of general practice. Much of the information on which the book is based comes from authoritative source material produced by the BMA.

Because the book provides an outline and summary of its various subjects, the reader is told at the beginning of chapters where to go for further information, advice and assistance.

I am grateful to Dr Ian Bogle for writing the Foreword, to John Lindsay, head of the BMA's Superannuation Department, for his comments on Chapter 14 and to Frank McKenna, head of the BMA's Private Practice and Professional Fees, for comments on Chapter 11.

I wish to thank the Editorial Board for their helpful comments on the text. I am, of course, responsible for the book's errors and omissions.

Finally, I am particularly grateful to the publisher, Andrew Bax. His energy and enthusiasm, and that of his team of colleagues, particularly Kathryn Shellswell who helped type the manuscript, have greatly encouraged me during the preparation of this book.

NORMAN ELLIS
July 1994

1 Independent Contractor Status

Where to obtain advice and assistance

GP principals or doctors seeking to become principals can seek the advice of their Local Medical Committee (LMC) secretary. Additionally, BMA members should contact their local BMA offices for expert advice and assistance. Help can also be obtained from FHSA and LMC offices.

Further reading includes *Making Sense of the Red Book: second edition*, Radcliffe Medical Press, the Red Book itself and the NHS (General Medical Services) Regulations 1992.

An independent contractor is a self-employed person who has entered into a contract for services with another party. This contract for services is fundamentally different from the contract of service which governs an employee–employer relationship. A key test, often used to distinguish between these two types of contract, relates to the question of 'control'. Generally, the more control A exercises over B's work, the more likely A is to be the employer and B the employee. Thus, if A can tell B not only what job to do but how it is to be done, A has sufficient control to make him B's employer.

However, if the exercise of control is much more diffuse, such that the person doing the work is not told how to do it, the contract is for services and the relationship is between what is confusingly known in legal terminology as 'the principal party' and 'an independent contractor'. Obviously, this test is crude and there are borderline cases, but the status of the National Health Service (NHS) general practitioner (GP) as an independent contractor has not been seriously questioned in the past. As an independent contractor, a GP should not be told by the Family Health

Services Authority (FHSA) or Health Board how to practise. FHSAs and Health Boards should seek to persuade and advise, not direct or control.

British general practice has been strongly influenced by the independent contractor status of its practitioners. The remuneration system, the organization of practices into partnerships, together with the medico-political institutions that enable GPs to exercise professional self-government, illustrate this influence.

As independent contractors, GPs exercise discretion and freedom in how they run their practices. This autonomy carries with it the administrative and financial responsibility for running the business itself and also responsibility for the clinical services provided. These responsibilities include providing premises, staff and equipment. If GPs were employees (like hospital consultants), an NHS trust or health authority would be responsible for providing these resources.

The main advantages of an independent contractor service are its flexibility and adaptability, and its capacity to offer a more personalized model of care. It also provides opportunities for innovation and diversity without interference, and gives patients scope for choice. Disadvantages can arise if the standards of service are allowed to vary widely. Those who are responsible for administering GPs' contracts sometimes see this arrangement as untidy and unsatisfactory, mainly because it lacks the means of control available to an employer.

No other occupation (apart from the other family health services contractor professions – dentists, chemists and opticians) has this unique partnership with the State, or with the public. In current parlance, general practice could be said to be the original 'privatized' sector of the NHS. GPs in other Western developed economies, together with most other professionals, such as dentists, lawyers, architects, surveyors and accountants, are also independent contractors. In Britain, GPs have jealously guarded their independent contractor status ever since Lloyd George's national insurance scheme was introduced in 1913. Although the profession supported the idea of a State-funded medical scheme, it was adamantly opposed to a salaried service; it recognized that the loss of independent contractor status would undermine its freedom to practise without State interference and ultimately put patient care at risk. GPs feared that government would seek to direct them in their day-to-day treatment of patients. This commitment to the independent contractor status underlies the policy of the Conference of Representatives of Local Medical Committees (LMCs).

The implementation of the 1990 contract has changed the relationship between individual GPs and FHSAs and Health Boards. New controls are being exercised by FHSAs and Health Boards over the work of GPs. They are now required to submit an annual report to the FHSA/Health Boards giving information on their practice arrangements, and also have to provide a detailed statement of the hours they are available to patients for surgery consultations, clinics and home visits.

Additionally, the 1990 contract specifies more precisely which services GPs are required to provide for patients, which procedures should be undertaken and which patients should be offered which services. For example, the terms of service have been amended to make clear that health promotion and illness prevention fall within the remit of general medical services. The services that are required of the GP are spelt out in some detail.

During the debate on the imposition of the 1990 contract, the question was raised as to whether the new regulations and terms of service were incompatible with the GP's status as an independent contractor. Whilst there can be no doubt that greater control is now exercised over the work of the GP, both the Government and the General Medical Services Committee (GMSC) of the British Medical Association (BMA) are agreed that the GP should continue to work as an independent contractor: indeed, in a joint statement from the Health Department and the GMSC, the Secretary of State for Health 'confirmed that the independent contractor status of GPs would not be affected'.

However, the question of whether GPs are independent contractors is not something which can be resolved by the declared wishes of the two parties directly concerned. It depends ultimately upon whether the control exercised by FHSAs and Health Boards is sufficiently diffuse to justify retention of the independent contractor status.

In spite of the increased accountability required under the new contract – and the increased powers of FHSAs and Health Boards – there should be no doubt that GPs remain independent contractors. The old contract also contained detailed specification of certain clinical tasks (such as those relating to the provision of maternity care) and these have never been regarded as being incompatible with the independent contractor status.

2 How GPs' Pay is Determined

THE Doctors' and Dentists' Review Body (DDRB) was set up in 1960, as a consequence of the recommendations of a Royal Commission known as the Pilkington Commission. Its remit is to recommend to the Prime Minister the levels of remuneration of doctors (and dentists) working in the NHS.

The Pilkington Commission was concerned to ensure that doctors' pay should not be used as a means of regulating pay movements in the economy; it wanted to see their pay removed from the political arena. The Commission considered various options, including direct negotiations, collective bargaining through Whitley machinery (used by most health service employees), and arbitration. It finally recommended an independent review body and laid down its ground rules (*see* Box 2.1).

How the Review Body system works

Although the Review Body is willing to receive evidence from any interested party, it concentrates on evidence from a few key sources (*see* Box 2.2). Both sides, the professions and the Health Department, normally submit written evidence to the Review Body on the same day, and also exchange evidence. This means that each side prepares its evidence 'in the dark' without sight of the other's evidence.

The next stage involves oral hearings. The Review Body meets each side, using the occasion to clarify any subject raised in the written evidence or to discuss other points of concern. The parties will also use the oral sessions to emphasize or update any matter in their written evidence.

Having considered all the evidence, the Review Body reports in confidence to the Prime Minister. Further time usually elapses before the

Box 2.1: The Review Body's ground rules as laid down by the Pilkington Commission

- the Review Body's main task was to exercise 'good judgement'
- although the government had the ultimate power to decide, Review Body recommendations must only be rejected by government very rarely, and for most obviously compelling reasons
- government should deal with Review Body recommendations promptly
- the remuneration of doctors should be determined primarily, though not exclusively, by external comparison with other professions and similarly qualified employees
- doctors should not be used by governments as part of their machinery for regulating the economy; they have a right to be treated fairly and the profession should assist the Review Body by willingly providing information about earnings
- doctors' earnings should not be determined according to short-term supply and demand considerations

Box 2.2: Main sources of evidence to the Review Body

- written evidence from the medical profession prepared by the BMA
- written evidence from the dental profession
- written evidence from the Health Department
- joint written evidence agreed between the profession and the Health Department, usually dealing with matters already agreed in negotiation
- jointly agreed statistical information, e.g. evidence on GPs' earnings and expenses
- independent evidence prepared by the Review Body's secretariat (Office of Manpower Economics), e.g. various surveys conducted at the request of the Review Body

report is published and the government announces its decision on whether to implement the recommendations.

GPs' remuneration

As independent contractors, GPs are paid a gross income by the NHS, out of which they meet practice expenses, including such items as staff salaries, the cost of surgery premises, and motoring expenses. The GPs' payment system is based on a principle known as 'cost plus'; the payments received are intended both to cover their expenses and to provide a net income.

The Review Body recommends what it considers to be an appropriate level of net income for GPs, and taking account of this recommendation the government decides upon the average level of income of all GPs. In fact, individual GPs receive greatly varying amounts depending upon the particular circumstances of their practices; expenses and list sizes differ and GPs provide a varying range of services. Virtually all GPs earn either more or less than the average; it is exceptionally rare to discover a GP whose earnings coincide exactly with the average figure.

The component for expenses should be added to net income. All expenses incurred by GPs in providing general medical services are paid back to the profession in full: some are paid directly to the individual GP actually incurring them (these are known as directly reimbursed expenses); the remainder of GPs' expenses are reimbursed indirectly on an averaging basis through fees and allowances. Thus, the exact amount an individual GP receives in indirectly reimbursed expenses will not, except by pure chance, equal expenditure, and in practice, there will be a strong incentive for a GP to economize on his or her own practice expenses.

Although this way of dealing with GPs' expenses is complex and can lead to anomalies and inequalities, it does recognize the independent contractor status of the family doctor, which is fundamentally different from that of salaried doctors employed elsewhere in the NHS. A possible alternative approach could have been to require each GP to submit to the FHSA or Health Board a monthly or quarterly claim for expenses, which it would check (and no doubt query on occasion). If this arrangement had been adopted, the profession would have given up its independence to choose how to run its practices. The significance of this is not always recognized by those who call for increased direct reimbursement.

It has been argued that because on average half of any practice's expenses are repaid indirectly through fees and allowances, irrespective of what it actually spends, the less an individual practice spends the greater will be its profits. Although there is some truth in this view, it does not represent the whole picture. GPs are directly reimbursed for part of the cost of providing many of the most costly items (for example, surgery premises and practice staff). A GP who chooses to underfund his or her practice will find it lagging behind other practices in the neighbourhood. A contrary and more positive view needs to be stated. If those GPs who are unwilling to invest in their own practices would overcome their reticence, the profession as a whole would benefit through the indirect reimbursement system and general practice would become more capital intensive. For example, if every GP decided to invest in an ECG machine, under the present system the NHS would have no option but to fund this investment through the indirect reimbursement scheme.

An explanation of how GPs' expenditure on defence body subscriptions is indirectly reimbursed illustrates this point. Almost every GP subscribes to a medical defence body and traditionally the amount each pays has been broadly similar. Thus, every GP is faced with an equivalent level of expenditure. These subscriptions have been paid ever since the present GPs' remuneration structure was established in the 1960s and therefore this expenditure is built into the system. The Review Body is aware that defence body subscriptions must be paid and that these have increased substantially. It is therefore able to make provision for this expenditure in its estimates of GPs' expenses, including an element to take account of anticipated increases in the subscription rate. As almost all GPs pay this subscription, it is reimbursed through fees and allowances (and because future increases have been taken into account) at close to the prevailing rate.

Expenditure that is fully and directly reimbursed

Certain practice expenses are reimbursed directly to each GP. However, while the direct reimbursement is treated as practice income, the expenditure is claimed against income tax. The GP's tax return may be used to calculate those expenses to be reimbursed indirectly through the fees and allowances. Direct reimbursements may be full or partial. Those items reimbursed directly and fully are listed in Box 2.3.

Full direct reimbursement of all of a GP's spending under any heading occurs only when the government or some public agency has direct control over its costs, as is the case with national insurance contributions.

Box 2.3: Items of GP expenditure that are reimbursed directly and fully

- surgery rent and uniform business rate, water rates, water meter installation and charges, and refuse collection charges
- employer's national insurance contributions in respect of GP trainees and some practice staff
- employer's pension contributions in respect of GP trainees and certain approved schemes for practice staff
- net ingredient cost plus VAT of drugs dispensed under the drug tariff

---

Likewise, the GP receives full direct reimbursement of surgery rent if the rent is approved by a district valuer. A GP trainer receives full reimbursement for the trainee's salary and car allowance, and employer's national insurance and superannuation contributions, again because all these costs are within the control of government.

Expenditure that is partially directly reimbursed

The most common partial direct reimbursement is the refund of practice staff salaries. Examples of allowances with maximum or fixed ceilings include those relating to the employment of an assistant, employment of a locum to cover a GP's absence because of sickness, maternity or study leave, and payments made under the doctors' retainer scheme.

The imposition of cash limits on the funds available to FHSAs and Health Boards for direct reimbursements means that the percentage of the salary refunded in respect of future staff appointments may differ from the fixed rate of 70% reimbursement paid under the former ancillary staff scheme. FHSAs and Health Boards can now exercise discretion in determining the level of direct reimbursements, and thus it may vary from zero to 100%.

A scheme for the partial direct reimbursement of computing costs was introduced in 1990, and provides for the direct payment of a proportion of the costs of purchasing, leasing, upgrading and maintaining a computer system.

Indirectly reimbursed expenditure

As described above, each year the Review Body estimates on the basis of a survey of tax returns, how much GPs as a whole will spend on providing general medical services. By taking into account the total FHSA/Health Board expenditure on direct reimbursements, it is then able to calculate an average figure for GPs' indirect expenses. This figure for average indirect expenses is added to the level of pre-tax pay which the Review Body considers appropriate for GPs to earn, known as net remuneration, and the resulting figure is called the gross remuneration. The various fees and allowances that comprise a GP's pay are then adjusted so that during the year they yield for the average GP the total gross remuneration which the Review Body has deemed appropriate.

This exercise is complex, and because the 'targets' set by the Review Body are not always met, any under- or over-payment is allowed for in subsequent years. As the Health Department is apprised of how much has been paid to GPs after the end of a financial year, it is not difficult to compare the level of average gross pay received with the original target. Average net pay is more difficult to calculate because it depends upon an analysis of income tax returns.

Because GPs wish to obtain tax relief, they inform the Inland Revenue of the expenditure they have incurred in providing general medical services. This is the key source of information for estimating GP expenses. Once a year, the Inland Revenue provides anonymized information relating to a sample of GPs' accounts, which includes all professional and partnership expenses.

GP accounts

As the level of expenses to be reimbursed is always based upon samples of income tax returns, it is vital that all GPs record their expenses correctly.

For revenue items, GPs should enter the full amounts of both directly and indirectly reimbursed expenses, including those items that may not appear in cash books, bank statements or cheque books. Examples include those payments made by FHSAs and Health Boards directly to health authorities or other bodies on behalf of the practice, such as health centre rents, waste disposal charges and levies. The practice of 'netting off' expenses against matching income must be avoided; failure to include expenses, however small, reduces the funding available to the profession as a whole.

Where capital items are concerned – for example, computers and equipment purchased from the practice fund management allowance – standard accounting practice should be followed. This will usually involve depreciating assets net of any government grant received.

3   GPs' Terms of Service

GPs working in the NHS have a contract with the FHSA or Health Board to provide general medical services for their NHS patients. It is important to note that this contract is with the FHSA or Health Board and not the patient, in contrast to most other countries where doctors have a direct contractual commitment to patients. Given this independent contractor status with a statutory authority within a publicly funded health service, it is not surprising to find that the NHS GPs' contract has been enshrined in legislation, the NHS (General Medical Services) Regulations (*see* Box 3.1).

The regulations, which include the GP's terms of service, provide the legal framework within which the business of NHS general practice is conducted. Because these regulations are laid down by Parliament their style is inevitably legalistic and makes them difficult for a layman to comprehend; a difficulty which is compounded by subsequent amending legislation. The regulations have been amended on many occasions; more than a dozen amendments were enacted after 1 April 1985 following the introduction of the limited list of NHS drugs. In November 1989 major amendments were introduced to implement new contractual arrangements

---

Box 3.1: National Health Service (General Medical Services) Regulations 1992

The regulations are in seven parts.

I General: citation and commencement; interpretation; scope and terms of service

II The Medical List: medical list; applying for inclusion or succession to a vacancy; amending of or withdrawing from it; removal from it; local directory of family doctors

III Medical Practices Committee: membership; reports; procedure for filling vacancies; certifying sale of goodwill not involved

IV General Medical Services other than Child Health Surveillance Services, Contraceptive Services, Maternity Medical Services and Minor Surgery Services: describes how patients apply to be on a doctor's list; how patients are assigned to doctors; the limits on list size; how patients transfer to another doctor; how patients are removed from a doctor's list; arrangements for temporary residents; temporary arrangements for running a practice

V Child Health Surveillance Services, Contraceptive Services, Maternity Medical Services and Minor Surgery Services: explains the separate lists for each of these services and how these services are obtained

VI Payments to doctors: requires the Secretary of State to publish the Statement of Fees and Allowances (the Red Book) and to pay doctors accordingly

VII Miscellaneous: whether a substance is a drug; appointment of medical advisers; guidance to doctors

---

with effect from 1 April 1990, and each GP was sent a copy of the amended terms of service. In April 1992 a completely revised and consolidated version of the regulations was made, and a copy of this was also sent to each GP. This new version rationalized the arrangement of the regulations and no longer includes the pharmaceutical services **regulations**.

Therefore, at the same time as the consolidated General Medical Services Regulations were published, consolidated pharmaceutical services regulations were also distributed. They included regulations governing the provision of pharmaceutical services by doctors, and how rurality is determined in relation to doctor and chemist dispensing.

There is an understandable reluctance to provide a definitive explanatory guide to the regulations. Since they carry the force of law, any dispute about their application or meaning can be resolved only by reference to the original text. Each copy of the regulations, and subsequent amending regulations, is accompanied by an official explanatory note, but it is always stated that this note does not form part of the regulations as such. Nevertheless, a doctor needs to know what is required to fulfil the contract with the FHSA or Health Board. In part, this knowledge is acquired from colleagues and partners, and the FHSA/Health Board. Advice from both LMCs and BMA local offices help to familiarize the doctor with the regulations and terms of service. Such advice should help a GP to be aware of current issues concerning their interpretation and application.

Every GP should have access to a copy of the principal regulations and any amending regulations. Copies are distributed by FHSAs and Health Boards and additional copies may be obtained from them. Nevertheless, many practices rarely refer to the regulations and, if a difficulty ever arises, a GP usually seeks advice from his or her LMC secretary or FHSA/Health Board general manager.

Alleged breaches of the terms of service by a GP are normally dealt with by the Medical Service Committee (MSC) of the FHSA/Health Board with which the GP is in contract. A separate set of regulations deals with the MSC procedure, the NHS (Service Committees and Tribunal) Regulations 1992.

It is essential that all GPs are aware of the General Medical Services Regulations because they contain the terms of service which form the basis of their NHS contracts. They should be referred to if any problems arise, and if there is any doubt about their meaning GPs should seek advice from their LMC.

The commentary below focuses on the main aspects of a GP's terms of service; it should help GPs to understand that section of the regulations (an appendix entitled schedule 2) which contains those terms of service. This selective commentary is not a substitute for the original text and should not be quoted if any problem arises.

The GP's terms of service

Professional judgement

When a GP has to decide what, if any, professional action needs to be taken under the terms of service, he or she is not expected to exercise a higher degree of skill, knowledge and care than may reasonably be expected of GPs generally. Any GP who wants clarification on a matter involving professional judgement should consult his or her LMC secretary or defence body. The same general principle also applies to GPs providing child health surveillance or maternity medical or minor surgery services; in each case the level of skill, knowledge and care expected is that which may reasonably be expected of any doctor included in the appropriate list.

Patients

The terms of service specify those categories of persons who are a GP's patients (*see* Box 3.2). Most are self-evident. However, it is important to note that if a patient seeking treatment claims to be on a GP's list but fails to produce a medical card, and the GP has reasonable doubts about the claim, the GP should nevertheless provide treatment but is entitled to ask for a fee. If the patient is subsequently able to prove to the FHSA or Health Board that he or she is on the GP's list, the fee has to be refunded. In practice, few GPs levy this charge; it is likely to be misunderstood and is rarely worthwhile.

Providing child health surveillance and minor surgery

GPs on the FHSA or Health Board list may provide to a patient on their list (or on a partner's list or the list of a GP with whom they are in group practice) child health surveillance and/or minor surgery services, and be paid for these services.

A GP who has agreed to provide child health surveillance services should:

- provide those services listed in Box 3.3 below (except for any examination the parent refuses to allow) until the child attains the age of five years
- maintain the records specified in Box 3.4
- provide the health authority with the information specified in Box 3.5.

GPs who have agreed to provide minor surgery services should:

- offer to provide any of the procedures listed in Box 3.6 as appropriate
- if providing minor surgery services to a patient not on their list, inform the patient's GP in writing of the outcome of the procedure.

Box 3.2: Who are a GP's patients?

The main categories are:

- persons on the GP's list

- persons whom the GP has accepted or agreed to accept on the list whether or not the FHSA or Health Board has received notification of that acceptance

- for a limited period of up to 14 days, persons the GP has refused to accept on to the list, if they live in the practice area and are not on the list of another doctor in the same area, or persons the GP has refused to accept as temporary residents

- persons who have been assigned to the GP under Regulation 21

- for a limited period, persons about whom the GP has been notified that an application has been made for assignment to him or her

- persons accepted as temporary residents

- persons eligible for acceptance as temporary residents whom the GP agrees to take a cervical smear from, vaccinate or immunize

- persons to whom the GP is requested to give treatment which is immediately required owing to an accident or other emergency at any place in the practice area, or any persons to whom the GP agrees on request to give treatment which is immediately required owing to an accident or other emergency at any place in the FHSA or Health Board locality, provided that there is no other doctor at the time otherwise obliged and available to give treatment

- persons for whom the GP is acting as a deputy to another doctor under the terms of service

- persons whom the GP has been appointed to treat temporarily

- persons for whom the GP has undertaken to provide child health surveillance or minor surgery services

- women for whom the GP has undertaken to provide contraceptive or maternity medical services

- persons whose own doctor has been relieved of responsibility for them during hours arranged with the FHSA or Health Board, for whom the GP has accepted responsibility during those hours.

Box 3.3: Child health surveillance: services

These services comprise:

- the monitoring:
  - (i) by the consideration of information concerning the child received by or on behalf of the doctor, and
  - (ii) on any occasion when the child is examined or observed by or on behalf of the doctor (whether pursuant to sub-paragraph (b) or otherwise) of the health, well-being and physical, mental and social development (all of which characteristics are referred to as 'development') of the child while under the age of five years with a view to detecting any deviations from normal development
- the examination of the child by or on behalf of the doctor on so many occasions and at such intervals as shall have been agreed between the FHSA and the health authority, or by the Health Board, in whose district the child resides ('the relevant health authority') for the purpose of the provision of child health surveillance services generally in that district.

Box 3.4: Child health surveillance: records

The GP should keep an accurate record of:

- the development of the child under the age of five years, compiled as soon as is reasonably practicable following the first examination and, where appropriate, amended following each subsequent examination, and
- the responses (if any) to offers made to the child's parent for the child to undergo any examination.

Box 3.5: Child health surveillance: information

The GP should provide the health authority with the following information:

- a statement, to be prepared and dispatched to the relevant health authority as soon as is reasonably practicable following any examination, of the procedures undertaken in the course of that examination and of the doctor's findings in relation to each such procedure
- such further information regarding the development of the child while under the age of five years as the relevant health authority may request.

Box 3.6: Minor surgery procedures

Injections	intra-articular
	peri-articular
	varicose veins
	haemorrhoids
Aspirations	joints
	cysts
	bursae
	hydrocele
Incisions	abscesses
	cysts
	thrombosed piles
Excisions	sebaceous cysts
	lipoma
	skin lesions for histology
	intradermal naevi, papillomata, dermatofibromata and similar conditions
	warts
	removal of toe nails (partial or complete)
Curette cautery and cryocautery	warts and verrucae other skin lesions (e.g. molluscum contagiosum)
Other	removal of foreign bodies
	nasal cautery

Terminating responsibility for patients

GPs may apply to the FHSA or Health Board to have a patient removed from their list. This takes effect on the day when the patient is accepted by, or assigned to another doctor, or on the eighth day after applying, whichever is sooner. However, if a GP is treating the person when removal would normally take effect, the FHSA or Health Board should be informed and removal will take effect only on the eighth day after it receives notification that the patient no longer requires treatment, or upon acceptance by another doctor, whichever occurs first.

From April 1994, GPs may require the FHSA/Health Board to remove immediately from their list any patient who has given them reasonable cause to fear for their safety, including those who have shown threatening behaviour. The criterion is the GP's reasonable fear. Before immediate removal, the GP *must* inform the police of the incident. This is, in any case, good practice, since a criminal offence under the Public Order or Offences Against the Person Acts will usually have been committed. Having registered the incident with the police, GPs should notify the FHSA/Health Board of their wish to remove the patient; regardless of whether its offices are open at the time, the removal takes effect from the moment the message reaches the authority. Fax or telephone notification is sufficient, but this should be confirmed in writing. GPs are also required to notify the patient too, but this can be done by post, or via the police, as appropriate.

The right to remove a patient has to be set out against the duty of an FHSA or Health Board to assign a patient to a GP if the patient is not acceptable on a voluntary basis. In an area served by only one GP this can severely limit a doctor's right to remove a patient.

A GP may agree with a patient to stop providing her with maternity medical services and failing agreement, may apply for permission to terminate the arrangement. The FHSA or Health Board may agree to this after considering the views of either party and consulting the LMC. If the GP stops providing maternity medical services the patient must be told so that she can make alternative arrangements.

A GP's agreement to provide child health surveillance services may be terminated:

- by either parent or doctor
- if the child has been removed from the doctor's list (or his or her partner's list or that of a doctor with whom he or she is associated in a group practice)
- if the parent fails to respond within 42 days to an invitation to arrange for the child to attend for examination.

Again, the GP should inform the FHSA or Health Board and, where appropriate, the patient, if he or she no longer intends to provide these services.

Services to patients

GPs are required to provide for their patients all necessary and appropriate personal medical services of the type usually provided by GPs. These should be provided at the practice premises or, if the condition of the patient requires, where the patient was living when accepted as a patient, or elsewhere in the practice area. The GP is not required to visit or treat the patient at any other place, but care has to be taken to ensure that neither the GP nor a member of his or her staff implies there is a willingness to visit at an address outside the practice area. If this should happen, the GP may be bound by a duty to visit.

There is no obligation to provide contraceptive services, child health surveillance services, minor surgery services, or, except in an emergency, maternity medical services, unless the GP has previously agreed to do so.

The doctor should, unless prevented by an emergency, attend and treat any patient who comes for treatment at the places and during the hours approved by the FHSA or Health Board, other than a patient who attends when an appointment system is in operation and has not made an appointment. In these circumstances the doctor may decline to see the patient during that surgery period, providing the patient's health would not be put at risk and the patient is offered an appointment to attend within a reasonable time. GPs should take all reasonable steps to ensure that a consultation is not so deferred without their knowledge.

The regulations specify in detail certain services which a GP is required to provide which include:

- giving advice, as appropriate, to a patient about the patient's general health, and in particular about diet, exercise, the use of tobacco, the consumption of alcohol and the misuse of drugs and solvents
- offering patients consultations and, where appropriate, physical examinations to identify or reduce the risk of disease or injury
- offering patients, as appropriate, vaccination or immunization against measles, mumps, rubella, pertussis, poliomyelitis, diphtheria and tetanus
- arranging for patients to be referred to other NHS services
- giving advice to enable patients to obtain help from the local authority social services department.

Box 3.7: Important changes to the GP's terms of service in respect of out-of-hours services

At the time of writing the Government has just agreed to changes to paragraph 13 of the Terms of Service, which secure greater flexibility for GPs as to how they may best meet their out-of-hours responsibility.

The amendments to paragraph 13 emphasize that GPs themselves are responsible for judging whether or not a consultation is required, on the basis of the information available, and allow them a similar flexibility when deciding what would be the appropriate location for the consultation, whether it is provided by telephone, at the surgery (or some other clinical setting), or at the patient's home, or whether it requires a direct referral to hospital.

Newly registered patients

If a patient has been accepted on to a GP's list (or assigned to it) the patient should be offered a consultation within 28 days to:

- obtain details of the patient's medical history, and when relevant that of his or her family, relating to:
  - (i)   illnesses, immunizations, allergies, hereditary conditions, medication and tests carried out for breast or cervical cancer
  - (ii) social factors (including employment, housing and family circumstances) which may affect health
  - (iii) life-style factors (including diet, exercise, use of tobacco, consumption of alcohol, and misuse of drugs and solvents) which may affect health
  - (iv) the current state of the patient's health
- physically examine the patient:
  - (i)   measuring height, weight and blood pressure
  - (ii) taking and analysing a urine sample to identify the presence of albumin and glucose
- record in the patient's notes the results of this examination
- assess whether and to what extent personal medical services should be provided to the patient
- offer to discuss with the patient (or the parent of a child patient) the conclusions of the consultation as to the state of the patient's health.

When offering a consultation for this purpose, the GP should:

- provide a written invitation – or if the initial invitation is made orally, provide written confirmation
- record in the patient's medical records the date of each invitation and whether it was accepted
- where, as a result of making the invitation, the doctor becomes aware that a patient is no longer residing at the address given in the records, inform the FHSA or Health Board.

A GP is not required to offer a consultation to a newly registered patient if:

- he or she is a restricted services principal (i.e. a principal who has undertaken to only provide child health services, contraceptive services, maternity medical services, or minor surgery services, or some combination of these)
- the patient is a child under the age of five years
- the patient was, immediately before joining the list, on that of a partner and had already had a consultation of this kind during the previous 12 months.

If a GP assumes responsibility for a list of patients by taking on a vacant practice, or becomes responsible for a sizeable number of new patients over a short period, the GP can ask the FHSA or Health Board to defer the obligation to offer these consultations.

Patients not seen within 3 years

If requested to do so, a GP is required to provide to a patient on his or her list a consultation to assess whether personal medical services are needed, if the patient: `

- is between the ages of 16 and 75 years
- has within the preceding three years attended neither a consultation with nor a clinic provided by any doctor in the course of the provision of general medical services.

During this consultation the GP should obtain the information listed in Box 3.8 and offer a physical examination including the procedures listed in Box 3.8.

The GP should record the findings and assess whether the patient requires treatment.

Box 3.8: Patients not seen within 3 years: information to be obtained and procedures to be undertaken during the consultation

Where appropriate the GP should obtain from the patient the following details of his or her medical history and, if relevant to the patient's medical history, that of his or her consanguineous family:

(i)   illnesses, immunizations, allergies, hereditary diseases, medication and tests carried out for breast or cervical cancer

(ii)   social factors (including employment, housing and family circumstances) which may affect health

(iii)   life-style factors (including diet, exercise, use of tobacco, consumption of alcohol, and misuse of drugs or solvents) which may affect health, and

(iv)   the current state of the patient's health.

The GP should also offer to undertake a physical examination of the patient, comprising:

(i)   the measurement of blood pressure

(ii)   the taking of a urine sample and its analysis to identify the presence of albumin and glucose, and

(iii)   the measurements necessary to detect any changes in body mass;

record in the patient's medical records, the findings arising out of the details supplied by, and any examination of, the patient;

assess whether and, if so, in what manner and to what extent the GP should render personal medical services to the patient; and

in so far as it would not, in the opinion of the doctor, be likely to cause serious damage to the physical or mental health of the patient to do so, offer to discuss with the patient the conclusions the doctor has drawn as a result of the consultation as to the state of the patient's health.

Patients aged 75 years and over

The GP should offer each patient an annual consultation and a domiciliary visit (which may be combined) to assess whether any treatment is required. This offer should be made no later than 1 April 1995 to any patient over the age of 75 years on the GP's list on 31 March 1994. For a patient who attains the age of 75 years on or after 1 April 1994, the domiciliary visit and consultation should be offered within 12 months of the patient's 75th birthday. If a patient joins a GP's list and is already aged 75 years, the offer should be made within 12 months. The GP should make the offer in writing (or confirm it in writing if made orally) and keep a record of the date of the invitation and whether it was accepted.

The doctor should record anything which appears to be affecting the patient's general health, including:

- sensory functions
- mobility
- mental condition
- physical condition including continence
- social and physical environment
- use of medicines.

The GP should also record the findings of the consultation and offer to discuss with the patient any conclusions that have been drawn.

Absences, deputies, assistants and partners

Normally, a GP should give treatment personally. However in the case of general medical services, other than maternity medical services, child health surveillance and minor surgery services, the GP is under no obligation to do so if reasonable steps are taken to ensure continuity of treatment by another doctor acting as a deputy, irrespective of whether the other doctor is a partner or an assistant. In addition, if it is reasonable to delegate the clinical treatment to a person whom the GP has authorized and who is competent to carry it out (e.g. a qualified nurse), the GP may do so.

A doctor on the obstetric list should not, without the FHSA's or Health Board's consent, employ a deputy or assistant to provide maternity services who is not (or is not qualified by experience to be) included on the obstetric list, except in an obstetric emergency.

As for child health surveillance services, a GP who has agreed to provide these may employ a deputy or an assistant on a child health surveillance list, or with the FHSA's or Health Board's agreement another deputy or assistant. A GP who has agreed to provide minor surgery services may employ a deputy or assistant who is on a minor surgery list.

In general, GPs are responsible for the acts and omissions of any doctors acting as their deputies, whether the deputy is a partner or an assistant. They are similarly responsible for any person they employ or who acts on their behalf. *However, a GP is not responsible under the terms of service for the acts and omissions of a deputy who is on the list of the same or some other FHSA/Health Board.*

The FHSA/Health Board should be informed of any standing deputizing arrangements unless the deputy is the GP's assistant or is already on its medical list, and carries out these arrangements at the premises where the doctor normally practises. If a GP is absent for more than a week, the FHSA/Health Board should be told who is responsible for the practice during their absence.

Before entering into any arrangement with a deputizing service, GPs should obtain the FHSA's or Health Board's consent. When giving consent, it may impose conditions to ensure that the arrangements are adequate, but must consult the LMC before refusing consent or imposing conditions. The FHSA/Health Board is required to review any consent given or conditions imposed in consultation with the LMC, and may withdraw consent or alter the conditions. A GP may appeal to the Secretary of State against a refusal or withdrawal of consent, or the imposition or variation of conditions.

GPs should take reasonable steps to satisfy themselves that any doctor employed as a deputy or assistant is not disqualified from inclusion on the FHSA's/Health Board's list. The GP should tell the FHSA/Health Board the name of any assistant employed and when this employment ends. A doctor should not employ one or more assistants for more than three months in a period of 12 months without its consent, but before refusing or withdrawing consent, it must consult the LMC. (A GP may appeal to the Medical Practices Committee (MPC) against refusal or withdrawal of consent.) If consent is withdrawn, the decision will not take effect for a month; but if an appeal is made to the MPC against withdrawal and it dismisses the appeal, the withdrawal takes effect from a date determined by the MPC, not less than one month after the date of dismissal. (A doctor acting as a deputy can treat patients at places and times other than those arranged by the GP for whom he or she is deputizing although regard must be given to the convenience of the patients.)

Arrangements at practice premises

The GP should provide adequate accommodation at the practice premises having regard to the practice's circumstances and is required, on receiving a written request from the FHSA or Health Board, to allow the premises to be visited at any reasonable time by a representative of either the FHSA/Health Board or LMC, or both.

If a GP intends to run an appointment system (or succeeds to or joins a practice where one is already running), the FHSA/Health Board should be told about the proposed system or of any proposal to discontinue it.

With certain important exceptions, a GP should not, without the consent of the FHSA/Health Board (or, on appeal, the MPC), start to practise in any premises within one year of their having ceased to be occupied or used for practice purposes by another doctor who within one month of such cessation begins practising at a group practice premises, as a member of a group, or at a health centre less than three miles away from the original premises. (This does not apply if the former occupant gives written consent for another doctor to use the premises.)

Employees

Before employing any member of staff, the GP should ensure that the person is suitably qualified and competent to carry out the required duties. In particular, the doctor should take account of the employee's academic and vocational qualifications, training and previous experience. The GP should also offer the employee reasonable training opportunities.

Availability to patients

Any GP should normally be available at times and places approved by the FHSA/Health Board and inform patients of his or her availability. In general, it will not approve any application unless satisfied that the times proposed are such that the GP is normally available:

- 42 weeks in any period of 12 months
- during not less than 26 hours in any such week
- on five days in any such week
- with hours of availability which are likely to be convenient to patients.

There are important exceptions to this basic requirement:

- a GP may seek to be normally available for 26 hours over a four-day week, if involved in health-related activities other than providing general medical services to his or her patients (*see* Box 3.9 below, for a broad definition of health related activities). But the four-day availability will not be approved by the FHSA/Health Board if it considers that the effectiveness of the doctor's services to patients is likely to be significantly reduced or patients are likely to suffer significant inconvenience

- a GP may seek to be available for less than 26 hours a week, if practising in a partnership. In this case there are two options:
  (i)   less than 26 hours but not less than 19 hours
  (ii) less than 19 hours but not less than 13 hours
- two doctors in partnership may apply for FHSA/Health Board approval to be jointly available for 26 hours a week.

The NHS Executive has issued important guidance to FHSAs on the availability requirements of the 1990 contract.

Strictly speaking, under the regulations the availability in question has to be looked at on the basis of each individual doctor's application in respect of his or her hours and their convenience to patients. The regulations do not require FHSAs to take partners' availability into account,

---

Box 3.9: List of health-related activities

- activities connected with the organization or training of the medical profession
- activities connected with the provision of medical care or treatment
- activities connected with the improvement of the quality of such care or treatment
- activities connected with the administration of general medical services
- appointments concerning medical education or training
- medical appointments within the health service other than in relation to the provision of general medical services
- medical appointments under the Crown, with government departments or agencies, or public or local authorities
- appointments concerning the regulation of the medical profession or services on the MPC
- membership of a medical audit advisory group

but nor do they preclude them from doing so except in circumstances where:

- this would result in arrangements which were not convenient to the GP's own patients;

OR

- the GP whose application is being considered objects.

The Health Department's view is that, provided these circumstances do not apply, FHSAs may take account of partnership availability. Appeals made against their decisions on availability have highlighted several areas of uncertainty. The most common of these are summarized below.

- FHSAs *cannot* stipulate which specific days doctors must be available. Under the regulations it is for doctors to choose which days they wish to be available. The 'convenience to patients' rule then applies to the spread of the hours across the doctor's chosen days. They may not, for example, require a doctor to provide a surgery on a Saturday, if that doctor is already available on five other days each week.

- Many FHSAs have agreed local policies as to how they deal with applications by doctors for approval of hours of availability. Nevertheless, each application has to be considered individually against the requirements of the terms of service. They may not hold that a doctor's proposed hours are inconvenient merely because they do not meet local criteria. There must be a recognized procedure for looking at each doctor's individual circumstances and convenience to patients.

- The regulations do not specifically require doctors to work the *same* five days every week. There is therefore no bar on doctors working a rota system provided that it meets the 'convenience to patients' test; for example, a fixed and regular rota, which is easily understandable by, and is advertised to, patients.

- FHSAs have the authority, when approving a doctor's hours of availability, to make its approval subject to specified conditions. However, one such condition may *not* be that approval is limited to a certain period (e.g. approving the hours subject to a review in six months). Any conditions laid down must involve an amendment to the proposed hours of availability which, if accepted by the GP, would result in the hours being agreed.

- FHSAs do not have the authority to designate a doctor, who has applied on the basis of full-time availability, as a part-time doctor and to reduce rates of pay accordingly. They may *only* reduce rates of payment to those appropriate for GPs working part-time, where it is a condition imposed by the MPC that the doctor should work part-time.

- In the case of doctors applying for four-day availability it is not necessary for the 'health-related activities' concerned to be performed on the day for which relief is being sought. Provided these activities are on a fixed and regular basis, a doctor may be entitled to apply for reduced availability on the basis of the cumulative effects of such activities.

Practice area

A doctor may not open premises in an area where, at the time of the application, the MPC considers the number of GPs to be adequate. Subject to this condition, a GP may apply at any time to the FHSA for consent to alter the practice area. (If it refuses consent, the GP may appeal to the Secretary of State.)

Notification of change of residence

If a GP changes his or her place of residence, the FHSA/Health Board should be told in writing within 28 days.

Records

A GP should keep adequate records of the illnesses and treatment of patients on forms supplied by the FHSA/Health Board, and should send these to it on request as soon as possible. Within 14 days of being informed by the FHSA of a patient's death (or not later than one month after otherwise learning of it), a GP should return the records to the FHSA/Health Board.

Certification

A GP should issue to patients or their personal representatives free of charge the certificates listed in Box 3.10 if they are reasonably required. However, a GP is not obliged to do so if the patient is being attended by another doctor (other than a partner, assistant or deputy) or is not being treated by, or under the supervision of, a doctor. In certain circumstances, a GP may issue a statement, without an examination, advising the patient to refrain from work for a period of up to a month, provided a written report, not more than a month old, has been received from another doctor

---

Box 3.10: List of prescribed medical certificates

Purpose of certificate	*Relevant legislation*
1. To claim payment; to prove inability to work or incapacity, and to draw pensions etc.	Naval and Marine Pay and Pensions Act 1865
	Air Force (Constitution) Act 1917
	Pensions (Navy, Army, Air Force and Mercantile Marine) Act 1939
	Personal Injuries (Emergency Provisions) Act 1939
	Pensions (Mercantile Marine) Act 1942
	Polish Resettlement Act 1947
	Home Guard Act 1951
	Social Security Act 1975
	Industrial Injuries and Diseases (Old Cases) Act 1975
	Parts I and III of the Social Security and Housing Benefits Act 1982
	Parts II and V of, and Schedule 4 to, the Social Security Act 1986
2. To prove pregnancy so as to obtain welfare foods	Section 13 of the Social Security Act (1988)
3. To show fitness for inhaling analgesia in childbirth	Nurses, Midwives and Health Visitors Act 1979
4. To register a still-birth	Births and Deaths Registration Act 1953
5. To enable payment to be made to an institution or other person in case of mental disorder of persons entitled to payment from public funds	Section 142 of the Mental Health Act 1983
6. To prove unfitness for jury service	Juries Act 1974

continued overleaf

Box 3.10: *continued*

Purpose of certificate	*Relevant legislation*
7. To prove unfitness for medical examination	National Service Act 1948
8. To support late application for reinstatement in civil employment or notification of non-availability, owing to sickness	Reinstatement in Civil Employment Act 1944 Reinstatement in Civil Employment Act 1950 Reserve Forces Act 1980
9. To register as an absent voter on grounds of physical incapacity	Representation of the People Act 1983
10. To apply for exemption from charges for drugs, medicines and appliances	National Health Service Act 1977
11. To support a severely mentally impaired person's claim for exemption from paying the community charge	Local Government Finance Act 1988
12. To support a claim by or on behalf of a severely mentally impaired person for exemption from liability to pay the Council Tax or eligibility for a discount in respect of the amount of Council Tax payable	Local Government Finance Act 1992

at a hospital, place of employment or other institution. The other doctor should not be a partner, assistant or deputy.

Accepting fees

A GP must not demand or accept a fee or any other form of remuneration for any treatment, including maternity medical services, whether under the terms of service or not, given to a person for whose treatment he or she is responsible. Doctors must take all practical steps to ensure that any partner, deputy or assistant does not demand or accept any remuneration for treatment given to their patients unless, of course, the partner, deputy or assistant would have been entitled to charge if the patient had been on his or her own list.

There are, however, certain specific circumstances in which a GP may accept a fee. These are listed in Box 3.11.

There are other certificates and reports which are not part of a GP's NHS obligations to patients. Fees for these are a matter to be agreed between the GP and the patient; the BMA recommends fees for these procedures.

A doctor must not demand or accept a fee or other remuneration from a patient for prescribing or supplying any drug or chemical reagent or appliance, unless the patient requires it solely in anticipation of the onset of an ailment outside the United Kingdom for which he or she is not currently being treated.

Box 3.11: Specific circumstances in which a GP may accept a fee

- from any statutory body for services rendered for the purpose of that body's statutory functions

- from any body, employer or school for a routine medical examination of persons for whose welfare the body, employer or school is responsible, or an examination of such persons for the purpose of advising the body, employer or school of any administrative action they might take

- for treatment which is not of a type usually provided by GPs and which is given:
  (i) pursuant to the provisions of section 65 of the Act, or
  (ii) in a registered nursing home which is not providing services under the Act

  if, in either case, the doctor is serving on the staff of a hospital providing services under the Act as a specialist providing treatment of the kind the patient requires and if, within seven days of giving the treatment, the doctor supplies the FHSA, on a form provided by it for the purpose, with such information about the treatment as it may require

- under Section 158 of the Road Traffic Act 1988

continued overleaf

Box 3.11: *continued*

- from a dentist in respect of the provision at his request of an anaesthetic for a person for whom the dentist is providing general dental services
- when he or she treats a patient under paragraph 4(3), in which case he or she shall be entitled to demand and accept a reasonable fee (recoverable under paragraph 39) for any treatment given, if he or she gives the patient a receipt on a form supplied by the FHSA
- for attending and examining (but not otherwise treating) a patient at his request at a police station in connection with proceedings which the police are minded to bring against him
- for treatment consisting of an immunization for which no remuneration is payable by the FHSA in pursuance of the Statement made under regulation 34 and which is requested in connection with travel abroad
- for circumcising a patient for whom such an operation is requested on religious grounds and is not needed on any medical ground
- for prescribing or providing drugs which a patient requires to have in his possession solely in anticipation of the onset of an ailment while he is outside the United Kingdom but for which he is not requiring treatment when the medicine is prescribed
- for a medical examination to enable a decision to be made whether or not it is inadvisable on medical grounds for a person to wear a seat belt
- where the person is not one to whom any of paragraphs (a), (b) or (c) of section 38(1) of the Act applies (including by reason of regulations under section 38(6) of that Act), for testing the sight of that person
- where he or she is a doctor who is authorized or required by an FHSA under regulation 20 of the Pharmaceutical Regulations to provide drugs, medicines or appliances to a patient and provides for that patient, otherwise than under pharmaceutical services, any Scheduled drug
- pursuant to an arrangement with him or her for the provision of services in accordance with Regulation 23 of the NHS (Fundholding Practices) Regulations 1993

Prescribing and dispensing

A GP is required to supply drugs or listed appliances needed for a patient's immediate treatment before a supply can be obtained elsewhere. In the course of treating a patient under general medical services, a GP must not issue a prescription for a drug or other substance listed in schedule 10 to the regulations (the 'black list') for supply under the NHS. In the case of a drug listed under schedule 11 to the regulations, a doctor may prescribe only in certain circumstances. A GP may prescribe these items privately, but may not charge for doing so. The GP can only charge for the item itself if he or she is already entitled to dispense to a patient and the GP can only do so for a particular course of treatment.

Practice leaflets

A GP or partnership should prepare a practice leaflet including the information in Box 3.12.

The leaflet should be reviewed at least annually to maintain accuracy and an up-to-date copy should be made available to the FHSA or Health Board, each patient on the doctor's list and anyone who reasonably requires one.

Box 3.12: Information to be included in practice leaflets

Personal and professional details of the doctor:

- full name
- sex
- medical qualifications registered by the General Medical Council
- date and place of first registration as medical practitioner

Practice information:

- the times approved by the FHSA/Health Board during which the doctor is personally available for consultation by his patients at his practice premises
- whether an appointments system is operated by the doctor for consultations at his practice premises
- if there is an appointments system, the method of obtaining a non-urgent appointment and the method of obtaining an urgent appointment

continued overleaf

Box 3.12: *continued*

- the method of obtaining a non-urgent domiciliary visit and the method of obtaining an urgent domiciliary visit
- the doctor's arrangements for providing personal medical services when he is not personally available
- the method by which patients are to obtain repeat prescriptions from the doctor
- if the doctor's practice is a dispensing practice, the arrangements for dispensing prescriptions
- if the doctor provides clinics for his patients, their frequency, duration and purpose
- the numbers of staff, other than doctors, assisting the doctor in his practice, and a description of their roles
- whether the doctor provides maternity medical services, contraceptive services, child health surveillance services or minor surgery services
- whether the doctor works single-handed, in partnership, part-time or on a job-sharing basis, or within a group practice
- the nature of any arrangements whereby the doctor or his staff receive patients' comments on his provision of general medical services
- the geographical boundary of his practice area by reference to a sketch, diagram or plan
- whether the doctor's practice premises have suitable access for all disabled patients and, if not, the reasons why they are unsuitable for particular types of disability
- if an assistant is employed, details for him as specified in paragraphs 1–5 of this table
- if the practice either is a GP training practice for the purposes of the NHS (Vocational Training) Regulations 1979 or undertakes the teaching of undergraduate medical students, and the nature of arrangements for drawing this to the attention of patients

Inquiries about prescriptions and referrals

The GP should be prepared to answer any inquiries from the FHSA or Health Board relating to:

- any prescriptions issued
- referrals to other NHS services.

Annual reports

A GP or partnership should provide the FHSA or Health Board annually with a report containing the information in Box 3.13. The information in paragraph 3 of the table only needs to be supplied if the FHSA/Health Board requests it, having considered whether the information is available from another source and having consulted the LMC. The information in paragraph 4 of the table need only be supplied if the FHSA/Health Board requests it and if the GP is not supplying the information already in order to qualify for health promotion or disease management payments. Each report should be compiled for a 12-month period ending 31 March and should be sent to the FHSA by 30 June.

Conclusion

This commentary is selective, not comprehensive. Not all paragraphs in the terms of service have been covered and only a brief summary of those referred to has been provided. If any problem arises, a GP should refer to the regulations and if necessary seek the advice and assistance of the LMC secretary or BMA local office.

Box 3.13: Information to be provided in annual reports

1 particulars of the doctor's other commitments as a medical practitioner, including:

  (a) a description of any posts held, and
  (b) a description of all work undertaken

and including, in each case, the annual hourly commitment, except that where a doctor has notified the FHSA/Health Board of such other commitments in a previous annual report, the report need only contain information relating to any changes in those commitments

2 as respects orders for drugs and appliances, the doctor's arrangements for the issue of repeat prescriptions to patients

3 information relating to the referral of patients to other services under the Act during the period of the report:

  (a) as respects those by the doctor to specialists:
      (i) the total number of patients referred as in-patients
      (ii) the total number of patients referred as out-
           patients

by reference in each case to which clinical specialty applies, and specifying in each case the name of the hospital concerned; and

  (b) the total number of cases of which the doctor is aware (by reference to the clinical specialty) in which a patient referred himself to services under the Act

4 information relating to the numbers of patients on the doctor's list:

  (a) who are diabetic
  (b) who are asthmatic, and
  (c) to whom the doctor has given advice, in accordance with paragraph 12(2) of schedule 2, about:
      (i)   the patient's weight
      (ii) the use of tobacco, or
      (iii) the consumption of alcohol

4   Fees and Allowances

Where to obtain advice and assistance

Help can be obtained from FHSA/Health Board and LMC offices. BMA members can also contact their local BMA office for advice and assistance.

Further reading includes *Making Sense of the Red Book: second edition*, Radcliffe Medical Press.

The GPs' pay system is particularly complex and hard to understand. They earn their income from a range of fees and allowances. These are of four broad types: fixed allowances, capitation-based payments, item-of-service payments and bonus payments. They are set each year at levels which will both yield the finite 'pool' of money available to fund GPs' net income and meet those expenses not reimbursed directly by the FHSA/Health Board. The 'pool' which funds GPs' net income is calculated by multiplying average net remuneration by the number of GP principals.

If the relative level of any fee or allowance is altered (e.g. by increasing basic practice allowance or decreasing capitation fees), the remaining fees and allowances are changed so that the total amount of money paid out to GPs remains at the right level. Unless additional funds are specifically made available by government (colloquially known as 'new money'), according to the current pay system it is not possible to increase any specific fees or allowances without simultaneously reducing some other fee(s) so as to maintain the level of net remuneration.

This chapter outlines the main fees and allowances payable to GPs which were newly introduced or substantially modified by the 1990 contract. Full details of all fees and allowances are given in the Statement of Fees and Allowances (otherwise known as the SFA or Red Book).

Basic practice allowance

GPs qualify for the basic practice allowance (BPA) if their individual list size or partnership average list size is at least 400 patients; a GP with at least 400 patients is paid a BPA and its level increases with list size up to a ceiling of 1200 patients. Thus a lump sum is paid for the first 400 patients and additional capitation payments are then made for each patient between 400 and 600, 600 and 800, 800 and 1000, and 1000 and 1200. By weighting the level of these capitation payments in favour of the lower list size, the BPA is designed to compensate for the proportionately greater standing expenses incurred by a small practice than a larger one. The BPA is also weighted in favour of part-time GPs; that of a half-time GP is significantly greater than half that of a full-time GP.

Deprivation payments

GPs are paid a capitation based supplement to the BPA, known as the 'deprivation payment', for all patients living within an area classified as 'deprived' according to the Jarman deprivation index, whether or not the individual or family is actually deprived. This supplement is intended to reflect the higher workload associated with some categories of patients. GPs with individual or average partnership lists of less than 400 patients who are not paid a BPA, nevertheless qualify for deprivation payments for patients living in deprived areas. There are three levels of payment according to the degree of deprivation (as measured by the Jarman index) of the area where the patient lives.

Seniority payments

There are three levels of seniority payment:

- the first level is paid to a GP registered for 11 years or more and providing general medical services for at least 7 years
- the second level is paid to a GP registered for 18 years or more and providing general medical services for at least 14 years
- the third level is paid to a GP registered for 25 years or more and providing general medical services for at least 21 years.

Pro rata payments are made to part-time GPs and those full-time GPs not eligible for the full BPA. Job-sharers are assessed for the seniority payment on an individual basis and payment is reduced pro rata according to their hours of availability.

Capitation fees

The standard capitation fees are paid at three rates according to a patient's age: under 65 years, 65–74 years, and 75 years and over.

Registration fee

This is paid to a GP who carries out certain health checks on a newly registered patient (except those aged under five years), normally within three months of joining the list.

Postgraduate education allowance

The postgraduate education allowance (PGEA) is paid to any GP who undertakes a programme of continuing education; it is intended to cover any course fees, travel and subsistence costs.

To receive the full rate of the PGEA, GPs must demonstrate to their FHSA or Health Board that they have attended an average of five days training a year over the past five years. Although the amount of time spent on courses may vary from year to year, a GP is expected to achieve a reasonable balance between years. Courses are divided into three areas:

- health promotion and prevention of illness
- disease management
- service management.

To claim the PGEA, GPs have to attend at least two courses under each of the three subject areas over the five years preceding the claim. The length of course is not actually defined in the Red Book; postgraduate deans have discretion to determine what constitutes a 'course' for the purpose of completing a balanced educational programme.

A GP should claim the allowance from the FHSA/Health Board each year, giving details of courses attended over the five-year period. Any GP who meets the required criteria (25 days training and at least two courses under each of the three headings) is paid a full PGEA in quarterly instalments. Lower levels of the allowance are paid if courses are spread across only one or two of the subject areas or less than the maximum length of training is undertaken.

Target payments for childhood immunization and cervical cytology

In 1990 the Government introduced target payments for childhood immunization and cervical cytology. There are two levels of payment. For childhood immunization, a higher level of payment is made to GPs who achieve 90% coverage and a lower level for 70% coverage. For cervical cancer screening the upper level is 80% and the lower 50%. These are calculated on a partnership basis.

Childhood immunization

There are two target levels, 70% and 90%, and these relate to average coverage levels across three groups of immunizations:

- Group I   – diphtheria, tetanus and poliomyelitis
- Group II   – pertussis
- Group III   – mumps, measles and rubella (MMR).

A target is reached if, on average across the three groups, 70% or 90% of the children aged two years on a GP's list have had complete courses of immunization (i.e. three doses of diphtheria, tetanus and poliomyelitis, or three doses of pertussis, or one dose of MMR). To calculate this, the coverage level in each group is taken into account and the mean of these is the overall coverage level. For example, if a practice has 10 children on the list aged two years all of whom have had complete courses of diphtheria, tetanus and poliomyelitis, nine who have had a complete course of pertussis and eight who have had the MMR immunization, the overall coverage level is nine out of 10, that is 90%. Thus, the higher target level has been reached. All complete immunization courses count towards coverage levels whether done by the GP making the claim or some other person, such as a community health clinic doctor.

The maximum payment a GP can receive depends on how many children aged two years are on the list; the Red Book describes how this is calculated. The proportion of the maximum payment made to a GP reflects the amount of this work done within general medical services, rather than in a clinic or hospital setting, whether in the patient's current practice or a previous one. Thus, if the 90% level is achieved, and GPs have done 70% of all the complete courses of immunization, the claiming GP receives 7/9 of the maximum payment.

Since 1 July 1994, Hib vaccinations have been incorporated into this target payment scheme, and the level of target payments have been increased to reflect the additional workload.

Pre-school boosters for children under five years

Again, there are two target levels: 70% and 90%. A target is reached if at least 70% or 90% of children aged five years on a GP's list have had reinforcing doses of diphtheria, tetanus and poliomyelitis immunizations. The arrangements for calculating these payments are similar to those described above.

Cervical cytology

There are two target levels: 50% and 80%; a target is reached if 50% or 80% of women on a GP's list aged 25–64 years in England and Wales (or aged 21–60 years in Scotland) have had an adequate cervical smear test during the previous five-and-a-half years. (This period is based on a five-year call/recall system with an allowance for unavoidable delays.) All smear tests are counted, not just those taken in general practice. For the purpose of calculating coverage, women who have had hysterectomies (involving the complete removal of the cervix) are excluded.

The maximum size of the target payment a GP can receive depends on the number of eligible women on the list. The actual proportion of the maximum payment paid to a GP reflects the work done by GPs (and their staff) as opposed to others, such as the private sector and community health services.

Allowances for teaching undergraduate medical students

GPs who assist university departments of general practice in teaching medical students, by providing experience of general practice are paid an allowance based on the numbers taught and time spent in the practice.

Child health surveillance fee

To be paid for child health surveillance GPs must be on the FHSA/Health Board child health surveillance list; admission to this requires them to satisfy the criteria relating to experience and training set out in the regulations. A capitation supplement is paid for each child patient under the age of five years to whom a GP provides developmental surveillance, if the child is registered with the GP for this purpose.

Minor surgery payments

A sessional payment is made to GPs on the FHSA/Health Board minor surgery list who personally provide minor surgery services. A session consists of at least five surgical procedures, performed either in a single clinic or on separate occasions. GPs can undertake minor surgery for patients on their own personal list or that of a partner or another member of the group practice. A GP is eligible for no more than three such payments in respect of any one quarter. However, a GP who is in a partnership or group may claim additional payments, provided the total number of payments to the partnership or group per quarter does not exceed three times the number of GPs involved. Up to four minor surgery procedures can be carried forward for inclusion in the following quarter's claim.

Night visit fees

GPs are paid a fee for each visit requested and made between 10 p.m. and 8 a.m. to a patient who is:

- on their list of patients
- a temporary resident
- a woman for whom they had undertaken to provide maternity medical services in connection with which the visit is made.

A fee is also paid if, in the patient's interests, the GP provides treatment at the surgery during these hours. Where the surgery is a treatment room of a GP hospital, the fee is paid only if the GP is not on duty or on call for the hospital and the request for this patient to be seen did not come from the hospital. However, if the GP visits the patient in a hospital to provide maternity medical services, a night visit fee is paid if he or she holds an appointment at the hospital, but was not on duty at the time, or if he or she does not hold such an appointment in respect of maternity medical services.

The higher fee is paid to the GP with whom the patient is registered, if the visit is made by:

- the GP with whom the patient is registered
- a partner or another GP from the group practice
- an assistant employed by a member of the partnership or group
- a locum or deputy employed by the partnership or group
- a trainee GP employed by the partnership or group
- a non-commercial rota of 10 or fewer GPs.

For all other visits (e.g. by a commercial or co-operative deputizing service) the lower fee is paid.

Associate allowance

Single-handed GPs in very isolated areas (e.g. the Highlands and Islands) are eligible for an associate allowance, enabling them, in conjunction with other single-handed GPs, to employ an associate GP who can provide services for patients during absences for social and professional purposes.

Health promotion payments

A new payment system based on practices developing health promotion programmes was introduced in July 1993 to replace previous payments for health promotion clinics. The new scheme is based on three bands of health promotion activity each corresponding to a payment level. The amount a practice receives is related to list size.

The content of each band is:

- band 1 – programme to reduce smoking
- band 2 – programme to reduce mortality and morbidity of patients at risk from hypertension and with established coronary heart disease (CHD) or stroke (subsumes activities in band 1)
- band 3 – programme offering a full range of CHD and stroke prevention (subsumes activities in bands 1 and 2).

There are separate payments for organizing chronic disease management programmes for either asthma or diabetes. These require practices to develop guidelines for delivering care to these patients.

Other fees and allowances

- additions to the BPA for employing an assistant
- inducement payments
- initial practice allowances
- mileage payments – these are no longer restricted to rural areas
- temporary resident fees
- fees for emergency treatment
- fees for immediately necessary treatment
- fees for maternity medical services
- fees for contraceptive services
- fees for public policy vaccinations and immunizations
- fees for service as an anaesthetist and for arresting a dental haemorrhage
- payments for supplying drugs and appliances
- payments during sickness and confinement – there are no list size restrictions for employing a locum during confinement
- locum allowances for single-handed practitioners in rural areas attending educational courses
- prolonged study leave allowance
- trainee practitioner scheme payments
- doctors' retainer scheme payments
- payments under the rent and rates scheme
- improvement grants
- payments under the practice staff scheme
- payments under the computer reimbursement scheme.

Claiming correct fees and allowances

The NHS GPs' remuneration system is probably the most complex in the world. It takes several hundred pages and an estimated 350,000 words of the regulations and the Red Book to determine how and what a GP should be paid. Every practice should ensure that it is claiming correct fees and allowances, otherwise it will not receive its correct remuneration. Conversely, no claim should ever be made, whether knowingly or unknowingly, for a fee or allowance to which a GP or practice is not entitled. A false or improper claim can have very serious consequences; FHSAs have not hesitated to instigate criminal proceedings against GPs who have made these.

5 The Partnership Agreement

The partnership provides a legal framework within which most GPs work: less than 10 per cent of practices are single-handed. Given its importance to the business of general practice, the widespread ignorance and neglect of the partnership agreement among the profession is quite remarkable.

Many practices do not have written partnership agreements; it has been estimated that at least half either have no written agreement or work to an outdated version. Any partnership without this essential documentation is susceptible to the vagaries that flow from the fact that relations between the partners are strictly controlled by a century old statute, the Partnership Act 1890. A partnership without a written agreement is known as a 'partnership at will' and is governed by this Act; its main characteristics are listed in Box 5.1. However, a partnership can develop or agree to abide by rules which modify or add to those drawn from this legislation. Variations and departures from the Partnership Act can be inferred from the conduct of the partners; for example, although the Act requires profits to be shared equally, many practices opt for a different basis of division.

Given the dangers and potential difficulties of a 'partnership at will', it is surprising how many practices do not have written agreements. But neglect of essential paperwork has been commonplace in general practice; until comparatively recently most practice staff did not have written employment contracts, even though they were legally entitled to them.

Box 5.1: Key characteristics of a 'partnership at will': one without a written agreement

- entire partnership ends automatically upon death, retirement or bankruptcy of any one partner
- any partner can choose to end the partnership immediately without notice to the other partners, unless remaining partners elect to continue
- all partners must have free access to the bank account and are entitled to take part in managing the business
- partnership decisions may be made by a majority of the partners, except that all partners must consent to a new partner being admitted as well as any change in the nature of the business
- no partner can be expelled from the partnership
- partners must not compete with the partnership; if they engage in any business on their own account in the same broad field of activity as the partnership, any income from this must be paid to the partnership
- all partners are regarded as 'agents' of the partnership and can take decisions and enter into commitments to which the partnership is bound

---

The need for a written agreement

A partnership in any field can be plagued by problems, and general practice is no exception. Although a written agreement offers no panacea, it at least lays down ground rules which can help to resolve, if not avoid, problems. Once these rules are established, it is only sensible to take a step further by writing them down clearly and unambiguously so that all partners know exactly where they stand.

Partnership disputes are widespread and can present particularly intractable problems. GP partnerships typically experience enough problems and difficulties in normal times; the imposition of the 1990 contract has added greatly to these by imposing extra pressures on practices and many partnerships have been tested to destruction by its exigencies. Whilst an agreement cannot prevent disputes, it can help to avoid many common problems and frequently resolve those which occur by specifying procedures to be followed when a dispute arises or a partnership breaks up.

A written agreement should not slavishly follow some prescribed standard format, but it must reflect the explicit wishes of the partners; only they know how they want to work together, the practice's circumstances and what problems need to be addressed.

What should be included in a written agreement

No written agreement, no matter how comprehensive can be expected to define all the rights and obligations of the partners; many of these have to be inferred from their day-to-day working relations. Nevertheless, there is a well-established framework that is widely used and this normally includes the clauses covered by the headings in Box 5.2 opposite. Strictly speaking many standard clauses covered by these headings are not necessary because the rights or obligations they assign are either prescribed by the Partnership Act 1890 or are always implied – for example, the obligation to be just and faithful in all dealings with one's partners, and to act in good faith towards each other (see Box 5.3). Nevertheless it is probably advisable to include them in the agreement.

A written and comprehensive partnership agreement should ensure equity for all partners and reasonable security. Equity does not necessarily imply equality; an equitable partnership agreement should ensure that all partners are treated fairly. For example, the list sizes of individual partners should have no significance in respect of each partner's rights and obligations. It is taken as evidence of good faith if a new partner is able to acquire a comparable list size as soon as reasonably practicable.

The notes below outline issues that need to be addressed and what should be covered under each heading.

Date, name, title and address

Any agreement should specify a date of commencement which may be earlier than the current date if it reflects an existing partnership, or a later

Box 5.2: Main headings in a partnership agreement

- date of document
- name, title and address of the partnership
- date when partnership commenced
- nature of the practice's business
- duration of partnership
- practice premises
- partnership capital
- partnership expenses
- partnership income
- sharing the profits
- attending to the affairs of the practice
- managing practice staff
- partnership decisions
- partnership taxation
- holidays and study leave
- maternity provisions
- prolonged incapacity and sickness
- voluntary and compulsory retirement from the partnership
- restrictive covenants
- defence body membership
- banking arrangements
- accounts
- arbitration/conciliation

date if it relates to a new partnership. It must be signed by all partners before it is dated; any liability will begin on the commencement date, not the date of agreement, unless both are the same.

The agreement should also include the name under which the partnership will practice, and the addresses of the surgery premises. If the partnership uses any name which does not consist of the true surnames of all partners, the true names of each partner must be included on letter headings, invoices, etc. and displayed in each surgery, to meet the requirements of the Business Names Act 1985.

Box 5.3: A breach of good faith

A new partner joins a practice with a satisfactory partnership agreement. After two or three months, he suggests to the senior partner that it would be a good idea to employ a further practice nurse, adding that he knows someone who would be suitable. The senior partner agrees, and the practice nurse is taken on. The nurse becomes pregnant, and it is revealed subsequently that she is the live-in girlfriend of the new partner. According to the senior partner, a lot of patients are outraged by the situation, and he insists that the nurse stops work and, in fact, wants to dismiss her. According to the partnership agreement, no member of staff can be dismissed without the agreement of all the partners, and therefore the nurse remains on the payroll until such time as she goes on maternity leave. On the basis of advice from the partnership's solicitors, the other partners override the junior partner's opposition on the grounds that his original action, in recommending his girlfriend as an employee without disclosing his relationship with her, was in breach of the obligation to act in good faith towards his partners.

From the BMA's files ...

The nature of the business

A possible wording for this clause is that the partners 'will carry on the profession of NHS general medical practice'. It is essential to specify the nature of the business because this limits the extent to which each partner is liable as an agent of the firm. Otherwise, the liabilities arising from some other quite separate and extraneous business activity undertaken by one partner might be incurred by the other partners, even though they had no direct interest or involvement in this other business. Box 5.4 illustrates the kind of problem that can arise.

Duration of partnership

There is no advantage in limiting duration; doing so reduces the security of all partners and can encourage them to compete among themselves in anticipation of the agreements termination. Thus a partnership should be

---

Box 5.4: Extent of a partnership's liabilities: a partner's wider interests

A GP of 15 years standing, who had worked solely in a three-man practice, started a business outside the practice with which the other two partners had no dealings, financial or otherwise. In 1991, two years after the business started, it went into receivership ...

The GP's assets were liquidated to satisfy his personal debts, and these included his share in the partnership business, its equipment, premises, etc.

From the BMA's files ...

Box 5.5: Duration of partnership

The Partnership Acts 1890 states that every partnership is dissolved in respect of all partners by the death or bankruptcy of any partner, unless there is agreement to the contrary. This is why every partnership agreement covering more than two partners should include a provision to the contrary.

'The partnership shall continue during the joint lives of the partners. The death, retirement, expulsion or bankruptcy of any partner shall not determine the partnership as regards the other partners'.

---

of indefinite duration: for the joint lives of all partners, or any two or more of them (*see* Box 5.5). However, once a partnership is created, it can be dissolved at any time by mutual consent.

Practice premises

An incoming partner should clarify ownership of surgery premises and any prospective liability to purchase a share. If the existing partners have a large investment in property and are seeking a contribution from a new partner, then he or she should seek advice about funding from an accountant, a lawyer or both.

> **Box 5.6: Valuing the premises**
>
> A practice agreement should specify the basis on which the premises will be valued if a partner dies or resigns. Whatever basis is used, the agreement should state that goodwill must be excluded from the valuation.

A new partner who is buying an equal share of the premises is entitled to an equal share of FHSA or Health Board direct reimbursement under the rent and rates scheme, even though parity in profit share may not be reached for several years. This important matter is often neglected if a practice simply treats this reimbursement as income and pays it into the partnership account before calculating profit shares.

The agreement should specify which partners are 'property owners'. If there is a lease or licence arrangement between the property-owning partners and other partners, it should be made only on the basis of legal advice. It is preferable that the agreement defines the owners and confirms the rights of the others to use the practice premises, and that the remaining partners should have a continuing right to use the premises for, say, three months if the property owner(s) leave the partnership.

Rent and rates payments from the FHSA or Health Board should normally be paid into the partnership's bank account, being the property of the partnership as a whole (*see* chapter 6 for a description of alternative ways of distributing these payments among partners, depending upon their shares in ownership of the property).

Partnership capital

This normally includes all property, equipment, drugs, surgery fittings and furniture, together with any cash used as working capital. An incoming partner will buy a share of these assets and also contribute to the practice's working capital. Partners normally own shares of the assets (apart from the premises) in the same proportion as their share in the profits. The written agreement should specify how shares in the partnership's capital are divided among the partners (*see* Box 5.7), what constitutes the capital, and also confirm the arrangements for expanding the capital.

Box 5.7: Acrimony over who owned what

Dr A fell out with his partners Drs B and C, and as a consequence, dissolution of the partnership was discussed. There had been considerable discontent between the partners which arose from a long period of study leave taken by Dr A. The partnership did not have a written agreement. When discussions took place about the partnership break-up, it was extremely difficult to disentangle the capital of the partnership from items individually owned by the partners. This sadly led to the demeaning scene of Dr A arguing in front of patients with Drs B and C over who owned which items of surgery equipment and furniture.

There was no statement of the capital assets and no inventory which the three partners could use in their discussions about dissolution. Consequently, the process was accompanied by considerable acrimony.

From the BMA's files...

Partnership expenses

The agreement should specify which expenses should be paid by the partnership as a whole; typically these should include the cost of practice staff, accounting and banking services, telephone and stationery, and also the costs of occupying and running the premises (rent, rates, heating, lighting, cleaning and maintenance). All these shared expenses should be met before profits are calculated and distributed, and partners should contribute to them in proportion to their profit shares.

Other expenses, such as the costs of the partners' cars and house telephones, are normally paid by individual partners because this arrangement is usually fairer. Whichever arrangement prevails, it should be specified clearly in the agreement so that there can be no ambiguity and uncertainty about this crucial matter.

Partnership income

It is generally held to be advisable to include all earnings from professional practice in the partnership's income, otherwise individual partners might be encouraged to concentrate on those activities rewarded by personal rather than practice income and even compete among themselves for this type of work. However, it is possible with care to arrange a partnership's affairs to enable partners to retain their non-general medical services professional income and not to put the harmony of the partnership at risk.

Certain earnings are normally retained personally because they should not put at risk the collective efforts of the partnership (e.g. the seniority and postgraduate education allowances). Whatever arrangement is agreed, it must be equitable and should be defined in the partnership agreement (see Box 5.8).

Box 5.8: 'A postgraduate experience'

A new partner unwittingly signed a partnership agreement which allowed the other two partners to retain their seniority allowances and PGEAs, but required her PGEA to be paid into the 'pool' for distribution among all partners.

From the BMA's files...

Dividing the profits

Stated simply, the profit (or loss) is the difference between practice income and expenses. The agreement should specify the size of each partner's share of the profits, and how it is calculated and paid. If changes in the share ratios are planned (e.g. a move to parity for a new partner), these need to be stated, including when they should take effect.

Under NHS regulations, for the FHSA or Health Board to recognize GPs as partners, it must be satisfied that they discharge the duties and exercise the powers of a principal in the partnership and that, unless an approved job sharer, they are entitled to a share of the profits (see Box 5.9) based on one of these options:

- if contracted to be available for at least 26 hours a week – a share of not less than one third of the partner with greatest share
- if contracted to be available for between 19 and 26 hours – not less than one quarter of greatest share
- if contracted to be available for between 13 and 19 hours – not less than one fifth of greatest share.

If any partner's share is grossly out of line with his or her contribution to the work of the practice, a concealed sale of goodwill may be deemed to have taken place (see Box 5.10).

Box 5.9: Salaried partners

This description is a contradiction in terms as far as it applies to any independent contractor. Someone is either a partner with all the rights and obligations which this entails, or they are not, in which case they are not a principal and the practice is not entitled, for example, to be paid a BPA (and its related allowances) for that doctor.

Box 5.10: Sale of goodwill is prohibited

The Medical Practices Committee (MPC) is responsible for issues concerning the sale of goodwill. Since 1948 GPs have been forbidden to sell the 'goodwill' of an NHS practice, 'goodwill' being the established custom of popularity of a practice. Examples of deemed sales of goodwill include:

- the premises are sold for substantially more than might have been expected if they had not previously been used for general practice
- a significant payment is made other than for undertaking partnership duties
- a partner receives a significantly less amount for his or her services than might reasonably be expected.

In particular, the MPC looks to see if the balance between profit share and workload is equitable.

The MPC may regard the following as evidence of a sale of goodwill:

- a new partner does not reach parity in the partnership profits within 3 years
- one or more partners is permitted to do less than a fair share of the practice workload
- one or more partners get longer or shorter holidays, or exceptionally is or is not entitled to study leave
- if, after a reasonable assessment period, a partner is restricted in taking onto his or her list any patient who chooses to register with him or her
- if the terms of expulsion, retirement or dissolution are not mutual.

Any GP about to join a practice who is concerned about a possible sale of goodwill may submit the terms of the proposed partnership to the Medical Practices Committee.

An incoming partner's share should be sufficient for it to be more than he or she might have earned as an assistant: this share should increase each year so that parity is reached within a reasonable time span, normally three years. He or she should not be prevented from taking a fair share of new patients onto his or her list (*see* Box 5.11).

Attending to the affairs of the practice

The agreement should state the time and attention which partners are expected to give to the work of the partnership, especially if one partner is allowed to give less time than others to it. If the partners are required to devote their whole time to the practice, it is advisable for the agreement to stipulate that they should not engage in any other business or accept any office (e.g. local councillor) without the consent of the other partners.

In the present climate, time spent on medical politics (e.g. as an LMC member or as a GMSC member) should be allowed for in the agreement, preferably before the issue has to be faced.

Managing practice staff

The agreement should specify who carries responsibility for staff matters. It is advisable that staff employed by the partnership should be engaged and dismissed with the consent of all partners, otherwise a dismissed employee could pursue a successful dismissal claim against the partnership as a whole if all partners have not agreed on the dismissal (*see* Box 5.13). It is also essential that the agreement should prevent one partner answering or sending letters concerning employment matters without the consent of the other partners. In any circumstances, hastily written and ill considered letters often cause problems.

Partnership decisions

According to the Partnership Act 1890 differences of opinion in the partnership are settled by majority decision unless the agreement specifies some other arrangement. A partnership must decide whether decisions are to be taken on the basis of majority voting and, if so, what size majority is required to endorse different types of decision.

Box 5.11: Exploiting a junior partner

Extract from an FHSA General Manager's letter:

"Dear Dr C
In reply to your request for information on the practice's arrangements for allocating patients to each partner's list, I can confirm that patients are divided:

Patients with surname	To doctor
A – end of Lane	A
Le – end of Watson	B
all remaining patients	C

I hope this information is helpful"

From the BMA's files....

Box 5.12: Discrimination is prohibited

It is unlawful for a partnership of any size to discriminate on the grounds of sex or marital status, and for a partnership of six or more partners to discriminate on grounds of colour, race, nationality (including citizenship) or ethnic or national origins:

- when appointing a new partner
- in the terms on which the new partner is offered a partnership
- by refusing, or deliberately neglecting, to offer a partnership

and where someone is already a partner:

- in the way he or she is afforded access to any benefits, facilities or services; or by refusing, or deliberately neglecting, to afford access to those benefits, facilities and services; or
- by dismissing the partner, or treating him or her unfavourably in any other way.

Box 5.13: Staff dismissal led to partnership rift

A busy urban four-doctor partnership decided to make several significant changes in the organization of its practice staff. These included introducing a new computer system, leading to an enlarged job description for the practice manager.

The senior receptionist was not happy about the changes and felt that the practice manager was usurping some of her work. Tension grew and came to a head when she had a blazing row with one of the partners. The latter discussed it with the other partner on duty and dismissed the receptionist that day. When the other two partners were informed, they felt the decision had been too hasty.

The senior receptionist immediately applied to the industrial tribunal claiming unfair dismissal. Strains appeared within the partnership and it split into two before the hearing. The two partners who had not been involved in the dismissal believed they had no responsibility or financial liability with regard to the industrial tribunal case.

The tribunal found in favour of the dismissed receptionist who was awarded almost £10,000. The doctors who had not been responsible for the dismissal believed that they were not liable for the payment. But lack of any reference in the partnership agreement to the dismissal of staff, meant that all four partners were jointly responsible and liable to contribute to the damages.

From the BMA's files ...

How this question is approached usually depends on partnership size. In a partnership of three, partners may opt for unanimity on all decisions, whereas a partnership of six may consider the unanimity is too difficult to achieve and may regard a majority of four to two as a satisfactory basis for decisions. Whatever approach is adopted should be specified in the agreement. Where there are job-share partners, the agreement should specify whether they exercise a half or whole vote each.

Irrespective of how a partnership approaches routine decision making, major decisions which affect key features of the agreement should be taken only if there is unanimity. The nature (i.e. what subjects they relate to) of such decisions should be defined in the agreement.

Taxation

Each partner is jointly and severally liable for the income tax on the whole of the practice's net profits and could be sued for this amount. In theory this is a formidable responsibility; the partnership agreement should therefore provide for enough funds to be set aside for tax liabilities, preferably in a separate bank or building society account designated for this purpose.

Under partnership law the admission or departure of a partner brings the existing partnership to an end and leads to the formation of new one. However, the partners may elect to be assessed for tax on the basis that the former business has continued. This continuation election must be made within two years of the date of change and must be explicitly agreed to by all members of the 'old' and 'new' partnerships, or in the case of a deceased partner, by a personal representative.

It is normally advantageous to a partnership to elect to be taxed on a continuation basis. However, this election can increase the personal tax bills of individual partners. It is preferable that the agreement requires a retiring or incoming partner to agree to making a continuation election,

---

Box 5.14: Paying somebody else's income tax!

Dr C, Dr D and Dr E were permitted to draw their full share of the profits. Each made his own arrangements to pay income tax and also indemnified the others against all such liabilities.

Dr D got into financial and marital difficulties which culminated in divorce. He is, among other things, forced to sell the matrimonial home which enables him to meet most of his personal debts but leaves him without further assets.

After informing his partners that he needs to get away for a while, he takes a holiday, goes abroad, and is never seen again. The Inland Revenue claim Dr D's outstanding tax from Dr C and Dr E, and they then realize that the protection they thought they had from their joint indemnities is no protection at all.

From the BMA's files ...

if asked to do so. Some partnerships indemnify a retiring or incoming partner against any additional personal tax liability that may result from it. It should be noted that in 1996/7 self-employed persons will be taxed on an actual and not preceding year basis, and also that partners' joint and several liability for the income tax due on the practice's net profits will no longer apply.

Holiday and study leave

Each partner's eligibility for leave should be on an equitable basis (see Box 5.15). When a locum is employed to cover holiday or study leave, expenses should normally be met by the partnership as a whole. It is advisable for the agreement to restrict the number of partners who can be on leave concurrently and the maximum length of unbroken leave which can be taken.

Box 5.15: Surprised by holiday arrangements

In a three-partner practice, a new partner signed a partnership agreement whereby he agreed to cover holiday periods etc. The three partners also agreed that they would cover each other's holidays to avoid the cost of hiring locums. Unfortunately for the new partner he had neglected to take account of the fact that the other two partners were married to each other and took their holidays together. As a result the new partner found himself providing continuous cover for the whole practice for at least six weeks each year.

From the BMA's files ...

Sickness and pregnancy

Partnerships can make various arrangements to pay for locums employed during prolonged absences. A simple method is for the absent partner to pay all the locum expenses. However, it is increasingly common for the partnership as a whole to pay the first few weeks of these expenses.

A partnership will infringe the Sex Discrimination Act if a pregnant partner is treated less favourably than a male partner with a distinctly male incapacity. Therefore a partner on maternity leave should not have to meet the full cost of a locum unless this arrangement also applies to

---

Box 5.16: Recommended maternity leave arrangements

- 14 weeks absence should be regarded as a minimum entitlement and the pregnant partner should have the right to determine for herself when the period of absence should start, in consultation with her own GP

- the practice should consider the question of funding the cost of a locum to cover the actual workload of the pregnant partner not merely her hours of availability

- the partnership should agree on a maximum period of absence following which the partner's failure to return to work may justify compulsory expulsion from the partnership

- the exercise of a partner's right to maternity leave should not abolish her entitlement to *pro rata* holiday and sickness leave

- adoption: the partnership agreement should specify leave arrangements

A partnership agreement which provides for maternity leave on terms which are less advantageous than sick leave could be construed as evidence of indirect sex discrimination.

---

sick leave. Box 5.16 outlines the BMA's recommended maternity leave arrangements.

Additional payments made by the FHSA or Health Board during sickness or confinement should be paid to the absent partner if he or she is responsible for locum expenses.

The question of how long the partnership or the individual partner pays locum expenses needs to be decided in relation to the arrangements for insurance cover for income protection and/or locum expenses.

Leaving the partnership

The agreement should specify the conditions under which partners may retire, including the required period of notice. It is usually simpler if the period of notice expires on a quarter-day so as to coincide with quarterly FHSA or Health Board payments. Ideally, a retiring partner should be allowed some discretion in selecting a date for retirement which is most favourable for tax purposes. The notice itself should not be less than three months because FHSAs and Health Boards are entitled to three months' notice before removing a GP's name from the NHS medical list.

According to the 1890 Partnership Act, a partner cannot be expelled by a majority decision unless the agreement permits this to happen. Thus the agreement should contain a clause which makes provision for the expulsion of a partner in specific circumstances such as prolonged incapacity, mental ill-health, removal or suspension from the medical register or NHS medical list, gross breaches of the agreement and bankruptcy. Although such a clause would confer a right to expel a partner in certain specific circumstances, like any clause it may be waived by mutual consent.

Most agreements require a partner to retire after a period of prolonged incapacity which prevents him or her from doing a fair share of the work for a period of six to 12 months. Naturally most partnerships wish to be as generous as possible in such circumstances, but because prolonged absence imposes a considerable burden on colleagues, it may be advisable to require an incoming partner to produce evidence of good health before the partnership agreement is signed.

Retirement

All GPs are required to retire from NHS practice by or on their 70th birthday. Thus it is sensible to include in the agreement a requirement that each partner retire from the practice by or on this compulsory retirement date. It may be advisable also to include a clause which allows a partner to continue to practice as a partner in a non-NHS capacity beyond a certain age, if other partners agree.

The partnership should agree on a clear and fair policy on retirement before individual problems arise; difficulties can occur if a practice only considers the issue of its retirement policy when the retirement of an individual partner is under discussion.

The issue of retirement can be particularly contentious for any partnership. Younger and older partners often express differing views on the subject, and a partner's perception of the issue may alter as retirement approaches. Young doctors entering a partnership often prefer a clause requiring compulsory retirement at a specific age such as 60 years, because it reduces the risk of them having to support an old and ailing partner who is increasingly unable to do a fair share of the work. Such a clause may be attractive to partners when they themselves are comparatively young, but it becomes less attractive as retirement approaches.

Restrictive covenants

NHS legislation prohibits the purchase or sale of goodwill, but did not abolish goodwill as such. Thus it is legal to protect goodwill by reasonable restrictions on the future activities of a departing partner. Such restrictions are commonplace and usually enforceable. But any restraint must be entirely reasonable.

Any restrictive covenant must apply equally to all partners and relate only to work normally undertaken by a GP, and its duration should not be too long. Any restriction from working in a defined area must be reasonable; there should be a significant number of patients near to the boundary and it should not include any large concentrations of population which are of little or no significance to the practice. It may be advisable for the agreement to refer to the practice area map which would normally be a reasonable area in which to restrict an outgoing partner from practising. The map itself could be included in the agreement.

It is preferable to have a limited restraint clause which is capable of being enforced rather than a more Draconian one which is unenforcable. Moreover, it is important to note that, in recent years, courts have taken an increasingly critical view of restrictive covenants.

The MPC has issued important advice on restraint clauses (*see* Box 5.17 below), particularly in relation to the length of time and distance specified.

Box 5.17: Restrictive covenants: advice from the MPC

- the MPC looks at restrictive covenants to see if they are reasonable and mutual in their application. If the provisions are regarded as unreasonable or too restrictive the MPC may consider this to be evidence of a sale of goodwill

- the MPC, in forming its opinion, normally regards as an acceptable upper limit a restrictive covenant which prevents a doctor engaging in NHS general practice and/or treating certain patients within a radius of two miles from the main premises for a period of two years. But variations may be justified by special circumstances

- the MPC would also consider there may be evidence of sale of goodwill if the radius and period were both reasonable but there was some extra restriction on a doctor acting within it in any capacity other than a GP; for example, if it prevented the doctor from filling a hospital appointment within the radius

---

Defence body subscriptions

Each partner should be required to be a member of a medical defence organization, or hold appropriate medical indemnity insurance whilst a partner.

Banking arrangements

The agreement should name the partnership's bankers and specify the arrangements for signing cheques. Normally the signatures of at least two partners should be required for all banking transactions and cheques over a specific amount.

Box 5.18 shows a not untypical inequitable agreement in respect of a partnership's banking arrangement.

Box 5.18: Extract from a partnership agreement signed in 1990

'The partnership bank account shall be under the sole control of the principal partner and any cheque thereon shall be signed by him alone and the junior partner hereby appoints the principal partner as his attorney for all purposes in connection with the operation of the said bank account and the signing of cheques drawn thereon'

From the BMA's files ...

Partnership accounts

The agreement should name the partnership's accountants and specify arrangements for drawing up the accounts, including the date of the practice's financial year. It is normal to require all partners to sign the annual accounts for them to be binding.

All partners must have free access to the partnership's accounts and records. Any denial of access to any partner is strong *prima facie* evidence that the doctor concerned is in fact an employee, not a partner. It may be advisable to include in the agreement a provision that all partners and their agents (e.g. personal accountants) should have copies of the accounts.

Arbitration

However carefully drafted, no agreement can cover all contingencies. Disputes and differences of opinion can occur even in the most harmonious partnership. Most should be resolved within the partnership, sometimes with advice or assistance from the local BMA office, or even with assistance from an independent conciliator. Traditionally, the BMA has advised doctors to make provision in their partnership agreements for disputes to be referred by mutual agreement to independent arbitration. In practice the use of arbitration should be very rare indeed. It is almost invariably an expensive process (usually much more costly than initially anticipated), more legalistic than is often assumed, and, perhaps more important, often accompanies a final breakdown in the partnership and therefore does not contribute to its continuation (*see* Box 5.19). Thus, though arbitration may be appropriate in certain specific circumstances, these are more limited that is generally assumed.

Box 5.19: Sledgehammer to crack a nut?

In a partnership of seven, a majority of partners (six to one) decided to purchase pregnancy-testing equipment to the value of £250. The one partner opposed was very unhappy with the decision. He deemed this expenditure to be unnecessary and inappropriate, believing the provision of a pregnancy-testing service would result in its use prior to abortion. He also objected to the provision of such a service free of charge. He could not prevent his partners from offering this service to their patients, but he did not see why they should be doing so at the expense of the partnership; that is, partly at his own expense. The matter was referred to arbitration. The arbitration decision was lengthy and costly, and led ultimately to the dissolution of the partnership. All parties incurred several thousands of pounds of legal costs and the only outcome was a dissolution which was also costly.

From the BMA's files ...

The best advice to follow is for all partners to consider carefully the possible consequences of any action they may be contemplating, individually or collectively, which may precipitate arbitration and lead ultimately to the dissolution of the partnership. Any type of legal action, including arbitration, is almost invariably a costly option and is often associated with the break up of the partnership.

6 Surgery Premises

NHS general practice differs from other professions in that a substantial proportion of the cost of providing premises is directly met from public funds. This is because successive governments have wished to ensure high standard surgery premises are generally available. Of course, NHS GPs also work within a different financial framework to those of other professions. They cannot simply raise income to fund premises by increasing their charges to clients, unlike for example accountants or solicitors. However, because public funds are at stake, the reimbursement of GPs' premises costs is subject to detailed and stringent controls, including rules specifying the amount of space eligible for reimbursement and how an appropriate level of rent reimbursement is assessed by the district valuer. In practice, no single element in the reimbursement scheme is free from public scrutiny or control. Box 6.1 below summarizes these controls.

GPs' terms of service require them to provide adequate surgery accommodation 'having regard to the circumstances' of the practice and to allow

---

> **Box 6.1: FHSA and Health Board controls over use of public funds for surgery premises**
>
> - government's district valuer advises on valuations to assess level of notional rent
> - government's district valuer advises on valuations relating to cost rent scheme
> - Red Book specifies minimum standards and maximum size of surgery premises eligible for reimbursement
> - 'prescribed percentage' set by the Health Department determines level of cost rent payments

this to be inspected by the FHSA or Health Board and/or LMC. Virtually every GP is eligible to be reimbursed rent and rates for their surgery premises. But the FHSA or Health Board has to be satisfied that the use of existing premises, their enlargement or a move to new premises, is in the interests of the NHS.

Although GPs can expect a high proportion of premises' costs to be directly refunded by the FHSA or Health Board, they often meet some of these costs themselves.

Surgery premises are usually provided in one of these ways:

- rented from a private landlord
- rented from a local authority
- rented from a health authority (often referred to as health centres)
- owner-occupied by an individual GP or partners
- newly developed under the 'cost rent' scheme and owner-occupied by an individual GP or partners, or rented from a third party.

Rented surgeries

GPs who rent a surgery from a landlord can recover the cost of the rent from the FHSA or Health Board. An appropriate rent, as assessed by the district valuer, is repaid in full. If the premises are not used wholly for NHS work (e.g. if a part is sublet), an equivalent proportion of the rent is not reimbursed.

Health centres

The rent of GPs practising from health centres owned by health authorities (together with their business and water rates) is normally paid by the FHSA or Health Board directly to the authority. Because it is not paid out from the practice's own funds and subsequently reimbursed, GPs should take particular care to ensure that both the rent and the equivalent amount of direct reimbursement are shown in their accounts. (Otherwise, if their accounts should be selected by the Inland Revenue for its anony-mized sample of tax returns, their actual expenses will be assessed wrongly and this will adversely affect the Review Body's estimate of the level of average expenses due to be repaid indirectly to the profession as a whole.) The practice accountant should understand why these payments and reimbursements must be shown correctly.

Owner-occupied surgeries

In many cases, surgeries will not be rented from a third party but owned instead by the GPs themselves, either individually or in partnership. A rent allowance (notional rent) is therefore paid to recompense them for the use of their privately-owned surgery for NHS purposes.

Notional rent allowance

Notional rent is paid on owner-occupied surgeries that are neither new nor developed within the scope of the cost rent scheme; it is based on a district valuer's assessment of the current market rent which may reasonably be expected to be paid for the premises. It is paid quarterly or monthly to the practice and is reviewed triennially. Until the recent decline in property values, this triennial review normally led to an increased notional rent and many practices became accustomed over many years to a steady increase in its level. Any practice which is not satisfied with its notional rent assessment may appeal against it.

Other reimbursements for premises

FHSAs reimburse other costs relating to surgery premises, as shown in Box 6.2.

Box 6.2: Rent and rates scheme: types of direct reimbursement

- cost rents
- notional rents
- uniform business rates
- water rates
- sewerage rates
- sewerage charges
- water meter installation costs and charges
- refuse collection charges

These payments should be regularly and correctly claimed; practices are known to have foregone many thousands of pounds of income because they have failed to submit claims.

Some FHSAs have introduced arrangements for paying rates and similar charges directly, which can improve a practice's cash flow. However, these payments and reimbursements, although they appear to be 'notional', must not be 'netted out' and thereby omitted from the practice's accounts.

Partnerships

It is usual for partnerships to own the surgery premises. But it is not uncommon for the partners to own them in differently sized proportions to the ratios which define their profit shares. For example, in a six-doctor partnership, two may be part-time or partially retired GPs not involved in surgery ownership, leaving the other four partners owning the building. One way of clarifying and simplifying ownership arrangements is to make a clear separation between the partnership formed for the purposes of providing general medical services, and that formed to own and run the premises. The 'clinical' partnership can then treat the ownership of the premises as a quite separate exercise from the profit sharing activities of the partnership. The 'property owning' partnership charges rent to the profit sharing partnership, which in turn receives notional rent income from the FHSA or Health Board. Alternatively, notional rent may be received by only the property owning partners.

Improvement grants

Grants are available for improving surgeries and these are subject to FHSA or Health Board cash limits in the same way as cost rent schemes and practice staff reimbursement. These grants are paid only if an FHSA or Health Board has given prior approval to an improvement scheme and if the same expenditure is not also claimed as allowable expenditure against income tax. GPs should obtain advice from their practice accountant on whether to opt for an improvement grant or a tax allowance. If part of the cost of an improvement project does not qualify for a grant, tax relief can be claimed on the residual amount.

Taxation

The notional rent allowance is paid to GPs whose privately owned surgeries are used for NHS general practice. It is essential for tax purposes that this is not treated or regarded as 'rent' in the usual sense of the word. In particular, it should not be treated as the private unearned income of GPs and it should not be included in the property section of the tax return. Otherwise, it could have a detrimental effect on how it is taxed and on whether retirement relief is granted for capital gains purposes.

New surgery development: the cost rent scheme

Most new or 'substantially improved' surgeries are funded by the cost rent scheme. Instead of being reimbursed at the current market rate (known as 'notional rent'), a GP may be reimbursed the cost of providing separate purpose-built premises (known as 'cost rent') if they are:

- completely new
- acquired and substantially modified
- already used and substantially modified.

An essential feature of the cost rent scheme is its recognition of the difference between the cost of providing an existing surgery and that of an entirely new or substantially improved surgery. It does not directly reimburse the actual interest paid on a loan for the cost of a building project. A practice should therefore ensure that its project is financially sound before entering into any commitment. It should be certain that the cost of servicing and repaying the loan can be met from the cost rent income, other practice income or (if necessary) funds from private sources.

The cost rent allowance is calculated by multiplying the cost of the project by a 'prescribed' percentage: for either a variable or fixed rate loan, according to the particular funding arrangement employed. To illustrate, if a project's total cost is £800,000 and the current fixed rate for the purpose of calculating cost rent is eight per cent, the annual cost rent payment to the practice is £64,000.

The four main cost components of a cost rent project are:

- buying the land
- erecting or modifying the building
- architectural and other professional fees
- bridging loan interest.

Because FHSA and Health Board funds for cost rent projects are cash limited, before entering into any commitments practices should:

- obtain FHSA/Health Board agreement 'in principle' to the project
- ascertain its priority in the FHSA/Health Board overall programme
- find out when cost rent payments will actually be made.

Not only must approval be obtained for the project, but the FHSA or Health Board should state whether it has sufficient funds for the scheme within its development programme and when they will be available.

The FHSA's or Health Board's formal written offer should:

- confirm that the project is accepted for cost rent reimbursement
- specify the method used to calculate the level of reimbursement
- give an interim estimate of the level of reimbursement (interim cost rent)
- give a target date when reimbursement should start.

This written offer will be conditional upon the project being completed within a given timescale; if this is not possible the FHSA or Health Board may withdraw approval (without any obligation to meet any expenses the practice has already incurred).

GPs must ensure that they have planning permission and that their architects are aware of the cost rent scheme, particularly its limits on size and building costs as set out in the Red Book. These cost limits are defined for each FHSA or Health Board and reflect regional variations in building costs.

Cost rent limits

The maximum amount that can be spent on building a surgery is strictly limited. Many practices find it difficult to keep within these limits and have had to finance significant shortfalls from their own resources.

When the FHSA or Health Board has determined the total costs that can be included in the scheme, it calculates the amount of cost rent to be reimbursed by multiplying that sum by a 'prescribed percentage'. There are two percentage rates 'prescribed' by the Health Department: a variable rate which is reviewed annually and a fixed rate which is reviewed quarterly.

The variable rate of reimbursement applies to projects funded by a variable rate loan, whereas the fixed rate applies to those wholly or mainly funded from a practice's own money or a fixed rate loan. If the fixed rate loan includes an option to switch to a variable rate, the fixed rate of reimbursement prevails until this choice is made.

Raising money for a cost rent project

When the project has been approved by the FHSA or Health Board, the next step is to raise money to fund it. Cost rent payments to a practice are calculated according to a fixed formula (which may be subject to some minor modifications) that takes no account of how the practice raises its funds. The actual process of obtaining the loan, and agreeing interest and repayment rates is a totally separate matter. This distinction is crucial. The 'prescribed' percentage rate is deemed by the Health Department to be a reasonable average level of return on capital; it takes no account of the idiosyncrasies of the loan market or the varying ability of practices to raise loans. Thus there may be a significant difference between the income received from the cost rent allowance and the expenditure incurred on the loan.

Banks, insurance companies and building societies provide long-term loans for cost rent projects. Although the mortgage offers security to the lender in the event of a practice defaulting on its loan, it could be argued that the actual 'security' is the income paid to the practice through the cost rent scheme. Normally this income will continue to be paid uninterrupted for as long as a surgery is deemed by the FHSA or Health Board as being used to provide NHS practice, unless the practice opts to change to notional rent. Nevertheless, the lender will wish to be satisfied that the practice can service and repay the loan according to its agreed terms, because the cost rent income can be less than the cost of servicing the debt. If there is a shortfall between cost rent income and loan repayment, this has to be met from practice income unless the partners have access to private resources. This current or future liability must be assessed at the outset by the partners according to their personal circumstances so that each partner can decide how the shortfall should be funded.

Changing to notional rent

The Red Book recognizes that current market rent (notional rent) is unlikely to produce initially a higher level of reimbursement than cost rent, therefore cost rent is paid until a practice opts to change to notional rent. But once this switch is made it cannot be reversed.

A review of notional rent can be requested:

- every three years from the operative date of the cost rent if the premises are owned by the practice

OR

- (if the premises are leased by the practice) when the rent due under the lease is reviewed or a new lease is entered into at the expiry of the existing lease.

Notional rent will be reviewed every three years after the date of assessment.

The decision to switch depends on several factors. Clearly, notional rent must exceed cost rent, and in the longer term a practice may feel relatively secure in the knowledge that property values and rents have (with some notable exceptions) tended to rise steadily year on year. However, recent years have witnessed a substantial decline in property and rental values. The average time taken for 'notional rent' to overtake 'cost rent' used to be in the range of seven to nine years. A significant problem has now arisen for those practices who switched from cost to notional rent three years ago, only to find that on triennial review the notional rent has fallen to a level which is below the original cost rent. There are GPs who are now finding that the value of their equity in the premises has fallen below their original investment and, instead of realizing a gain at retirement, are facing the prospect of having to repay a considerable sum to the partnership to reflect this.

Clearly, a practice should assess carefully at the time of review how much more reimbursement would be paid, likely future movements in interest rates and, the projected economic and political climate during the period prior to the next review of the prescribed variable rate.

7 Employing Practice Staff

As employers, GPs are subject to an extensive range of employment law; during the past 25 years some 16 Acts of Parliament have been implemented establishing over 20 new legal rights for individual employees. As a result of an important ruling by the House of Lords, unfair dismissal and redundancy rights will be extended to include anyone with two years' service who works eight hours a week or more. Box 7.1 below and the commentary in this chapter presuppose that the Government has enacted amending employment legislation to implement the House of Lords' ruling.

This plethora of legislation has been enacted by successive governments to encourage a more formal and equitable approach to industrial relations and personnel matters. Other influences on this legislation have included comparisons with international standards (e.g. the Equal Pay Act and Sex Discrimination Act, and recent European legislation on maternity leave) and legislation in other fields such as the Race Relations Act. Although this body of employment law is intended to influence personnel practices in all organizations, the special position of the small employer, whose circumstances and resources differ greatly from those of the large organization, has usually been ignored by legislators. There have been some recent

Box 7.1:

Individual rights	Eligibility (length of service)
To be given a minimum period of notice – based on length of service – of termination of employment	1 month
To be given written particulars of terms of employment	Immediately* for any employee working at least eight hours per week (the employer has two calendar months in which to supply it)
To receive equal pay with a member of the opposite sex doing similar work	Immediately
Not to be discriminated against on the grounds of marriage or sex	Any stage from advertising of job
Not to be discriminated against on the grounds of colour, race, nationality, or ethnic or national origins	Any stage from advertising of job
Not to be unfairly dismissed	Two years*+
To receive a guaranteed payment when no work is available	One month*
To receive payment when suspended on medical grounds – in certain specified industries only	One month
Not to be dismissed on pregnancy or childbirth grounds	Immediately

continued overleaf

Box 7.1: *continued*

Individual rights	Eligibility (length of service)
To take 14 weeks' maternity leave	Immediately
To take 40 weeks' maternity leave	Two years' service if working 16 hours a week or more (five years' service of working between eight and 16 hours a week)
To receive statutory payment for absence due to pregnancy or maternity	26 weeks
To return to work after absence due to pregnancy or maternity leave	Immediately
Not to have action – short of dismissal – taken against him/her because of trade union membership or activity	Immediately
To have time off – with pay – for carrying out trade union duties for approved industrial relations training, if trade union is recognized for collective bargaining purposes	Immediately
To have time off for trade union activities if trade union is recognized for collective bargaining purposes	Immediately
To have time off for public duties	Immediately

continued opposite

Box 7.1: *continued*

Individual rights	Eligibility (length of service)
To have time off – with pay – to seek alternative work or to arrange training if made redundant	Two years*
To have protection in case of employer's insolvency	Immediately
To receive an itemized pay statement	Immediately
To receive on request a written statement of the reason for dismissal	Two years* (immediately and automatically if for pregnancy reasons)
To have paid time off for antenatal care	Immediately
To have a protected period of notice and for his or her trade union – where recognized by his or her employer for collective bargaining purposes – to be consulted if made redundant	Immediately

* Employees working 8 hours or more a week are eligible.
+ If dismissal is for certain inadmissible reasons – that is, for reasons of trade union membership or activities, maternity or childbirth, or sex or race discrimination – there is no length of service qualification.

minor concessions to size, but nevertheless the totality of employment law imposes a far greater administrative burden on a small employer.

The overriding aim of any employer should be to avoid litigation. This can be achieved by good management practice which means taking a more formal approach to many employment matters, such as preparing written employment contracts. For instance, small businesses often fail to issue written contracts of employment to staff (even though the law requires that this should be done) and rely instead on informal and undocumented understandings, which are often a recipe for disaster.

This chapter summarizes the following key aspects of employment legislation:

- the employment contract: what it should contain and how to change it
- statutory sick pay
- statutory maternity leave and pay
- disciplinary and dismissal procedures
- discrimination.

The employment contract

A contract of employment exists as soon as an employee demonstrates an acceptance of an employer's terms and conditions of employment by starting work. Both employer and employee are then bound by the terms offered and accepted. Often the initial agreement is verbal not written, but within two months of an employee starting work the employer is legally obliged to provide a written statement detailing the main terms of employment, including a note on disciplinary procedures. (This requirement does not cover staff who normally work fewer than eight hours a week.)

This written statement must contain the following information:

- names of parties to the contract
- date employment began and statement about continuity of employment
- job title or brief description of the work
- place of work
- pay, scale or rate of remuneration, intervals between payment
- hours of work
- holiday entitlement and holiday pay

- sick pay and sick leave
- pension arrangements
- notice of termination or length of contract
- grievance, disciplinary and appeals procedures (employers with less than 20 employees are exempt from including information on the disciplinary procedure).

It is also advisable, though not obligatory, to include information on:

- retirement policy
- maternity provisions
- health and safety policy.

It is sensible to prepare and issue a comprehensive contract of employment that covers all these subjects. (BMA members can obtain a model employment contract from their local BMA office.)

Attention paid to preparing a correct contract of employment should prevent unforeseen and unwanted disputes. The actual process of preparing and agreeing a contract should ensure that the practice is reasonably familiar with its legal responsibilities and obligations, and has not unknowingly acted contrary to these at the outset. Moreover, if any dispute should arise and a practice has to defend its personnel practices and policies, its position is greatly strengthened if it can show that it acted in good faith and took reasonable steps to act in accordance with the law.

The statutory requirement to provide written statements on these matters does not have to be supplemented in any way. Although there is no legal obligation to provide a written contract as such, in practice a written statement of the main particulars of employment (together with a policy statement on health and safety) can be regarded as the basis of a written employment contract. The contract as a whole also includes the job description (whether written or not), and also the many informal and undocumented understandings and working practices which inevitably form an important part of any employment contract. An example of these informal and unwritten practices are the arrangements applying to staff coffee and tea breaks.

A written contract may have to be changed. No difficulties should arise if the correct procedure is adopted and the substantive reason for the change is 'reasonable'. There are various ways of changing a contract and the key underlying principle is that an employee should normally consent to any changes before they can become contractually binding, irrespective of whether this consent is implied or, by express agreement, given in advance of, or at the time of the change.

Obviously, an employer should seek to reach agreement on the proposed changes. If consent is obtained this can be given by express agreement, either orally or preferably in writing. In any case, an employer is required to put in writing the changed terms of the contract if they relate to any of the subjects listed above. Alternatively, consent may be demonstrated by implied agreement which can normally be assumed if an employee continues to work under the new contractual terms without complaint.

The written contract itself may contain provisions that allow for changes in matters such as pay, place of work, working hours and duties of the job. Nevertheless, even if a contract is drafted broadly, an employer must be prepared to show that the change itself is reasonable and was implemented in a reasonable way.

If consent is not forthcoming, even though the employer has made considerable efforts to agree the change with staff, unilateral implementation requires a reasonable period of notice. Normally, any contractual change imposed by an employer without an employee's consent will be a breach of contract, and if this is a fundamental breach (striking at the heart of the contract), an employee may be entitled to claim compensation for unfair dismissal. But by giving sufficient notice of the change, normally at least as long as that required to terminate the contract, it may be possible to avoid these problems. However, even if this length of notice is given, an employer could still be liable to pay compensation for unfair dismissal or redundancy. The advantage of giving adequate notice of change is that the employee is usually left with little or no time to protest after it is actually introduced.

In summary, the reasonableness of any change to an employment contract is subject to both a procedural test and a substantive test. Two questions have to be addressed and be capable of being answered in the affirmative:

- has the employer proceeded in a reasonable way by seeking agreement and giving adequate notice?
- is the proposed change itself a reasonable one to make in the particular circumstances of the business?

Statutory sick pay

The statutory sick pay (SSP) scheme establishes a minimum entitlement to sick pay for most employees. Every employer is required to pay sickness benefit as the agent of government, but the decision on whether to do so lies primarily with the employer rather than the Department of Social Security (DSS).

The main features of SSP are:

- National Insurance (NI) sickness benefit is no longer payable for most sickness absence; instead staff should receive SSP directly from their employer
- SSP is paid in the same way as normal pay and is liable to deductions for income tax and NI contributions
- entitlement to sick pay does not depend on previous NI contributions or previous service with the employer
- married women paying the reduced NI contribution and part-timers are entitled to SSP provided that their earnings are above a specified figure
- the total SSP that may be received from one employer for one or more periods of sickness cannot exceed 28 weeks' worth; after 28 weeks State benefit may be claimed from the DSS
- the employer has to decide whether sick pay is payable
- small employers can deduct 100 per cent of the amount paid out in SSP from remittances to the Inland Revenue for NI contributions
- SSP is paid at two rates according to the employee's average weekly earnings.

The rules of SSP are quite complicated and need to be applied correctly. Every practice should have a copy of the DSS's free booklet *Employers' Manual on Statutory Sick Pay*.

Statutory maternity rights

Most practices employ only a small number of staff, a majority of whom are women. The employment rights of the expectant mother are intricate and stringent; thus, any employer can face serious administrative problems if staff become pregnant.

The six main employment rights of the expectant mother are:

- not to be unreasonably refused paid time off work for antenatal care (applicable to all employees irrespective of length of service)
- to take 14 weeks' maternity leave
- to take 40 weeks' maternity leave and return to work if she works at least 16 hours a week and has at least two years' service (or between eight and 16 hours and five years' service)

- to receive 18 weeks' statutory maternity pay (SMP) if she has 26 weeks' recent continuous employment and normal weekly earnings above the NI lower limit
- to complain of unfair dismissal if dismissed because of pregnancy or childbirth
- to return to work after absence on account of pregnancy or confinement.

This area of employment law is complex for both employer and employee. It is vital that GPs obtain detailed guidance on how to ensure an employee obtains her statutory maternity rights; each practice should have a copy of the Department of Social Security free booklet *Employer's Manual on Statutory Maternity Pay*. Any mistake, even if due to ignorance or mis-understanding of the law, could lead to a tribunal case and costly compensatory award. Industrial tribunals are assiduous in upholding pregnant employees' rights and impose severe penalties in cases where unfair dismissals have occurred because of pregnancy or childbirth.

Disciplinary procedures and dismissal

Employers are required to include details of their disciplinary procedures, and the rules governing an appeal against disciplinary action, in their employment contracts, or to specify where these are to be found. (Although employers with fewer than 20 employees are exempted from this requirement it is advisable for all of them to do so.)

Disciplinary rules and procedures should promote fairness and order in the treatment of individual employees. They help a practice to run effectively by setting standards of conduct and performance, and ensuring that these are followed; they should not be seen primarily as a means of imposing sanctions. Their main purpose should be to emphasize and encourage improvements in individual employees' conduct and performance.

Employees who have not completed two years' continuous employment, or work fewer than 8 hours a week cannot normally complain of unfair dismissal, except if the dismissal is for an inadmissible reason such as pregnancy or childbirth.

The risk of a successful claim of unfair dismissal (which can involve compensation payments of several thousands of pounds) can be largely avoided if the procedure adopted is fair and reasonable, and the reasons for the dismissal are also fair and reasonable. A practice may have to justify its actions in an industrial tribunal so it is wise to keep detailed documentation throughout.

Several key principles relating to retiring age affect an employee's rights to complain of unfair dismissal:

- if normal retiring age is the same for men and women no one may complain of unfair dismissal after that age, whatever it is
- if there is no normal retiring age, anyone under the age of 65 years may complain of unfair dismissal
- if normal retiring age is discriminatory (e.g. 60 years for women and 62 years for men), anyone under 65 years may complain of unfair dismissal.

Normal retiring age is ascertained from the reasonable expectations of employees and may differ from contractual retiring age. It may also vary between posts and grades.

Redundancy

Redundancy is still rare among practice staff but it has become more commonplace as practices have adjusted to the exigencies of the 1990 contract. Regrettably, unfair dismissals on the pretext of redundancy are more common; it is often thought that redundancy offers a more palatable way of getting rid of an unwanted employee.

If a redundancy occurs, important legal obligations fall upon the employer. Employees have a statutory right to receive redundancy payments and paid time off from work to look for another job if they have at least two years' service and work at least eight hours a week. These same qualifying conditions also determine whether the employee has the right to claim unfair dismissal if a redundancy selection has not been made fairly according to objective criteria.

Under employment legislation redundancy is defined as a dismissal caused by an employer's need to reduce the number of staff. Normally an identifiable area of work should have disappeared or been reduced. A dismissal cannot be regarded as a redundancy if the employer immediately engages a direct replacement. But an employee with different skills or in a different location may be engaged (unless the redundant employee could be required under the contract of employment to work at the other location).

Normally any employee of a practice, when it changes hands, automatically becomes an employee of the 'successor' practice on the same terms and conditions of employment. It is as if the employee's contract had originally been made with the new practice; continuity of employment is preserved, as are any rights acquired under the old contract. So when staff are transferred in this way no dismissal has occurred and thus there is no entitlement to a redundancy payment.

An employer must make a statutory lump sum redundancy payment to any employee with at least two years' continuous service, working at least eight hours a week, who is dismissed because of redundancy.

Self-employed people or members of a partnership do not qualify. Employees on fixed term contracts of at least two years' duration which include, with explicit written agreement, a clause waiving entitlement to redundancy payments are also disqualified.

The amount of the lump sum payments depends on how long the employees have been continuously employed, how these years of service relate to particular age bands, and their weekly pay. An employee does not pay tax on statutory redundancy payment and an employer may set it off against tax as a business expense.

As far as possible, objective criteria, precisely defined and capable of being applied in an independent way, should be used when determining who is to be made redundant. This ensures that employees are not unfairly selected for redundancy. Examples of these criteria include length of service, attendance record, experience and capability. They should be applied consistently by any employer irrespective of the size of the business.

Great care must be taken if a practice is considering a redundancy, otherwise it could be faced with a claim for compensation for unfair dismissal. BMA members should contact their local office at the earliest opportunity for expert advice on how to handle this difficult situation. Far too often redundancy has been used as a pretext for dismissing employees who are not in fact redundant. The consequences of using redundancy to dismiss an employee who should otherwise be dismissed on grounds of inefficiency or incapacity, where there is no genuine redundancy, can be very serious indeed. A successful claim for unfair dismissal can require an employer to pay an employee a five figure compensatory award. This compensation cannot be offset against taxation, nor can any part of it be reimbursed by the FHSA.

Discrimination in employment

GPs rarely experience any difficulties with the race and sex discrimination laws. Of course, avoiding discrimination *per se* is good management practice. It may seem unlikely that a small business with only a small number of employees (most of whom are women) could be affected in any way. But both the Race Relations Act and the Sex Discrimination Act apply to all employers, irrespective of size. Previously the Sex Discrimination Act applied to all employers apart from those with five employees or fewer; the government recently removed this exemption.

There are two areas where legislation requires employers to act (and to be able to show that they have acted) in a manner that is not discriminatory on grounds of:

- sex and marital status
- colour, race, nationality (including citizenship) or ethnic or national origins.

If a practice's recruitment and selection procedures, together with its employment practices, are properly conducted no difficulties should normally arise. Although sex discrimination legislation was primarily intended to improve the employment status and opportunities of women, GPs, whose practice staff are almost exclusively female, should remember that men have equal rights under this legislation.

The scope and structure of both sex and racial discrimination law are similar. Both specify two types of discrimination (direct and indirect) and both require employers to take essentially the same action so as to ensure their employment practices are neither discriminatory in practice nor capable of being interpreted as such.

Direct discrimination occurs when a person treats another person less favourably on grounds of race (or sex, or both) than he or she treats (or would treat) someone else. It is not necessary to show that the person openly expressed an intention to discriminate: it is possible in many instances to infer that the motive was discriminatory in the light of the circumstances of his or her actions.

Indirect discrimination occurs when the treatment may be equal in a formal sense but is discriminatory in its effects on one sex or particular racial group; for example, an unnecessary stipulation that a cleaner should have certain educational qualifications (e.g. 'O' levels or GCSEs) which are not required for the job. When assessing whether an employer has acted in an indirectly discriminatory manner an industrial tribunal is required to consider whether his or her actions, although formally applied in a non-discriminatory manner, have the effect of being discriminatory.

There are three areas where it is unlawful to discriminate on grounds of race or sex when recruiting staff:

- in the arrangements for deciding who should be offered a job
- in relation to the contractual terms offered

- by refusing or deliberately omitting to offer a person employment.

It is also unlawful for employers to discriminate on grounds of sex or race in promotion or training opportunities, and in relation to any other benefits, facilities or services they provide for employees.

The most important matters on which a practice may need to concentrate are its arrangements for selecting and recruiting staff. The more informal its methods, the greater the risk of being accused of discrimination, particularly on grounds of race. An approach based on an informal 'word of mouth' method can easily leave an employer open to a claim (even from someone unknown to the practice who has not actually applied for a vacancy) that the selection procedure is discriminatory.

8 Health and Safety in the Surgery

> **Where to obtain advice and assistance**
>
> BMA members should contact their local BMA offices for advice and assistance. Local Health and Safety Executive (HSE) offices are also an important source of information, and provide a wide range of useful pamphlets and booklets.

GPs' duties as employers arising from the Health and Safety at Work (HSW) Act are neither difficult to understand nor hard to apply, but they must be given serious attention. Most surgery premises should conform to the requirements of the Act and its regulations and, apart from some minor (almost technical) matters, there is little in the legislation that should worry a typical practice.

The HSW Act is essentially a piece of enabling legislation which allows detailed parliamentary regulations to be enacted and then promulgated and enforced by the Health and Safety Executive (HSE). These regulations lie at the heart of most health and safety activity, spelling out in detail what is expected of employers.

HSE inspectors visit GP surgeries from time to time and the frequency of visits is increasing. This has caused some anxiety. This chapter provides guidance on those matters which HSE inspectors may wish to discuss; it does not provide a definitive statement or interpretation of the law.

The Act establishes powers and penalties to enforce health and safety standards. It requires employers to provide and maintain a safe working environment, and any proceedings that may be taken against them under the Act are criminal. An employee can report to the HSE a breach of an employer's statutory duty which may then bring criminal charges.

Like other employment legislation, the HSW Act pays little regard to the limited resources of a small employer. For example, many provisions are aimed at employers who recognize trade unions; the law states that trade union safety representatives and safety committees should be appointed if these are requested by a recognized union. However, even a typical practice, employing only a handful of staff who are not unionized has important duties to fulfil under this Act.

Employers' duties to their staff

The main thrust of the Act is to make both employers and employees more conscious of the need for safety in all aspects of the day-to-day working environment. Employers are required to do all that is reasonably practicable to ensure the well-being of employees.

What does reasonably practicable mean?

The words 'reasonably practicable' are important and their meaning can be construed from case law and the advice of HSE inspectors. A court's assessment of whether it was 'reasonably practicable' for an employer to avoid a particular hazard or risk of injury, usually takes account of the cost of preventative measures (particularly if an employer's resources are limited) and weighs this against the risk of injury and its likely severity.

Box 8.1:

The Act requires equipment and methods of working to be safe and without risk to health. Attention should be paid to waste-bins, electric typewriters, sterilizers, photocopying machines, heating equipment, computing equipment, furniture, fire extinguishers, electrical plugs and points, light switches, and any other equipment that may be hazardous. Particular importance is attached to maintaining and renewing equipment. HSE inspectors will want to look at your arrangements for servicing; for example, maintenance contracts for computers and servicing contracts for fire extinguishers. They will also be concerned with the age, reliability and positioning of equipment. Finally, they will wish to ensure that the health of staff is not put at risk by the use of VDUs.

But it is not enough to do, as Box 8.1 describes, what is necessary to ensure that equipment and methods of working are safe. Safe systems of working need to be both understood and applied by staff; for example, they should understand and follow stringent procedures when disposing of clinical waste.

Providing a written practice health and safety policy

The law requires employers to provide information, training and supervision for staff on health and safety matters. Unless a practice employs less than five staff, it is required to provide a written statement of its general policy on health and safety, and arrangements for implementing it. Practice staff should be consulted about the form and content of this statement.

The HSE discourages the use of 'model' statements such as the one provided in Box 8.2. This is because all employers should prepare their own; the HSE suspects that anyone who takes the easy option of copying a 'model' written statement is unlikely to have given serious attention to preparing and implementing their health and safety policy.

The 'written statement' should be simple and concise; long sentences and long words reduce impact. Nevertheless, safety rules should be clear and comprehensive.

The written statement may be included in each employee's written employment contract; in a small practice with less than five staff, a written statement could be posted in a public place, such as the staff notice board.

Safety officers

Safety officers and safety representatives are usually appointed only if an employer recognizes a trade union; they are most likely to be found in health centres where health authority staff work alongside a practice's own employees.

Staff who are appointed as safety representatives have considerable powers on health and safety matters; they can inspect the workplace, enquire into accidents, raise complaints directly with the GP, and insist on a joint staff–management safety committee being formed. In short, they have a legal right to challenge the employer on all matters relating to health and safety.

Because both employers and staff share a legal duty to promote the health and safety of everyone using the premises, the HSE recommends

---

Box 8.2: Health and safety in the practice: a specimen written statement

The partners' policy on health and safety is to ensure that the environment of all users of the surgery premises is as safe and healthy as possible. As a member of the staff you are expected to support this aim.

Your employer is ultimately responsible for your health and safety; however you also have a legal duty to take reasonable care to avoid any action or omission which might cause injury to yourself, your colleagues or other people using the surgery premises. In particular, you should not meddle with or misuse any clothing or equipment which has been provided to protect health and safety.

There are certain hazards which you should know about:

- prams and cycles parked on the premises
- medical equipment and instruments used in the consulting rooms
- cooking utensils and equipment used in the staff rest-room.

You must report any accident to the doctor in charge as soon as possible. You should then write down what has happened, explaining how the accident occurred, so that we can take steps to avoid its repetition.

---

that all employers should involve staff in developing and implementing health and safety policy and procedures. However, a safety committee is hardly feasible in a small practice. Instead, one member of the staff (e.g. the practice manager) could be appointed to serve as a 'safety officer' to monitor health and safety. But GPs cannot and must not simply pass over their responsibilities in this field as employers to their practice managers; they themselves must also be involved and, to ensure this happens, it may be advisable for the 'safety officer' to report directly to a partner on health and safety matters.

Duties to other users of the premises

Although the Act is mostly concerned with employees' health and safety, it also imposes a duty on employers to ensure the safety of other users of the premises, who include patients, pharmaceutical representatives, visitors, builders, trades people and health authority staff. If the premises are owned by a private landlord or local health authority, the licence or lease may impose this duty upon them and they may also be liable if there is an accident. The Act requires practices to ensure that all users are safe from the risk of personal injury. In particular, it may be necessary to consider whether the premises present any potential hazards to elderly or infirm patients. The Occupier's Liability Act 1957 already lays down a 'common duty of care' which is owed to all users of the premises.

Recording accidents and notifying dangerous occurrences

The legislation requires employers to record accidents and notify the HSE of certain serious accidents to any user of the premises (*see* Box 8.3 for the types of accident and dangerous occurrences which need to be reported). Normally the employer is responsible for notifying any accident; although there may be circumstances where the owner of the premises is responsible for doing so, it is best to assume that the employer should notify the HSE.

Employees' responsibilities

Employees are required to take reasonable care of their own health and safety and that of other users of the premises who may be affected by their actions or omissions. They are expected to cooperate with their employers in carrying out these duties. Although the duties of employees apply 'while at work', it would be wise to assume that these also apply throughout the time they are on the premises. This is important since accidents can occur when staff are preparing tea or lunch in a common room during rest periods.

Staff must not interfere with or misuse any equipment provided for the purposes of health and safety, such as fire exits and extinguishers, and warning notices. They must follow any safety procedures relating to the use of a kitchen, cloakroom or rest-room.

Box 8.3: Three categories of accidents and dangerous occurrences which may need to be reported

1 **Notifiable accidents.** These include fatal accidents (and those accidents that prove to be fatal within a year of their occurrence) and major injuries. A major injury is a fracture of the skull, spine, pelvis, any bone in the leg (other than in the ankle or foot), any bone in the arm (other than in the wrist or hand), amputation of a hand or foot, loss of sight of any eye, or any other injury that results in the person injured being admitted into hospital as an inpatient for more than 24 hours, unless that person is detained only for observation.

These accidents must be reported to the HSE if they occur to anyone on the premises.

There are two exceptions from the reporting requirements. In the event of injury occurring to a patient who is undergoing treatment in the surgery which is caused by the treatment, it should not be reported. Accidents to any self-employed person working on the premises, unless he is under the control of another person, are also excluded from the reporting procedure. But this exclusion is likely to end in the near future.

2 **Other accidents.** These do not have to be reported to the HSE. They include what are known in industry as 'three-day accidents'. This category only applies to the GPs own practice staff, not to other health authority employees working on the premises. These accidents are notified to the HSE by the DSS (not by the GP) only if the employee makes a claim for industrial injury benefit.

3 **Dangerous occurrences.** These mostly apply to industrial premises; few are likely to happen in GPs' premises. From the list of dangerous occurrences that have to be reported, only one type may be relevant. This is when a person is affected by the inhalation, ingestion, or other absorption of any substance, or lack of oxygen, to an extent that it causes acute ill-health requiring medical treatment. This could be caused by a defective central heating system.

How is the law enforced?

It is important to remember that the HSW Act is a criminal statute and the HSE is its enforcement agency. Failure to carry out any duty under the Act constitutes an offence and can lead to a prosecution, and a fine or imprisonment. However, the HSE is firmly committed to a philosophy of persuasion. It has discretion to decide whether to prosecute and only does so after very careful consideration of its inspectors' advice. If a prosecution should occur, a court normally assesses what preventive measures would be reasonably practicable given the available resources.

Each area of the country has its own inspectors some of whom will be specifically concerned with health service premises, including GPs' surgeries. They have considerable powers which are stated in their warrant of appointment; HSE inspectors may enter any premises to enforce health and safety legislation and do not need to seek permission before doing so. However, they should visit at a 'reasonable time' and when doing so they can meet and take statements from any user of the premises.

In practice, HSE inspectors telephone to arrange appointments. Very rarely 'surprise' inspections are made in response to a complaint from an employee or a user of the premises. Otherwise, the only reason why unannounced visits may be made is that an inspector has spare time available and includes visits to small premises (such as a practice surgery) within a schedule of visits to large establishments. These 'surprise' visits have caused anxiety among recipients. No offence is intended and inspectors should not be suspected of harbouring ulterior motives.

When the inspector calls

If there are five or more staff, the inspector will wish to see the practice's written statement of safety policy and instructions on safety procedures and its accident book. Since 1993 they are also looking for compliance with the requirement to carry out a risk assessment under the new Management of Health and Safety Regulations 1992. Increasingly, inspectors are looking for evidence of a good general approach to the management of health and safety; but the following may be among the specific requirements they will look for.

HSE inspectors will examine electrical equipment, which should be in good working order and covered by satisfactory maintenance arrangements. Toilet and washing facilities should be at least equal to those required in offices; in particular, there should be a supply of hot and cold running water and inspectors may even propose wrist-operated taps in all rooms used for treating patients.

Other matters which inspectors will also wish to assess include heating systems, VDUs, storage arrangements for drugs and vaccines, steam sterilizers, clinical waste disposal, and general heating and lighting standards.

What happens if the inspector is not satisfied?

When inspectors complete their inspections they normally raise any improvements required directly with the person in administrative charge of the surgery. If these matters are not of major importance, the inspector will simply request that they are carried out as soon as possible. But more serious matters could lead to a formal letter or even a written notice requiring them to be put right within a specified period of time of not more than 21 days. In these circumstances inspectors would also warn staff of their intention to serve a written notice. In the most unlikely circumstance of there being a serious risk to health or safety, which should never occur in a GP's surgery, the inspector can issue a prohibition notice. Where there is a very serious risk, all work has to stop immediately.

Keeping an accident book

All employers must keep an accident book to record accidents and notifiable occurrences. This enables these incidents to be monitored so that preventative action can be taken to avoid any recurrence.

COSHH regulations

The Control of Substances Hazardous to Health Regulations 1988 (COSHH) set out a legal framework for managing health risks from exposure to hazardous substances used at work. They aim to prevent occupational ill health by encouraging employers to assess and prevent or control such risks in a systematic and practical way. The regulations also apply additional obligations to employers to control hazardous substances and protect people exposed to them. They apply to most hazardous substances except those covered by their own legislation, such as asbestos, lead and material producing ionizing radiation. The regulations set out the measures employers (and sometimes employees) have to take. Any failure to comply with these exposes employees to risk and constitutes an offence under the HSW Act. Hazardous substances include those labelled as dangerous (i.e. very toxic, toxic, harmful, irritant or corrosive) under the statutory requirements.

The basic principles of occupational hygiene which underlie the COSHH regulations include:

- assessing the risk to health arising from work and what precautions are needed
- introducing measures to prevent or control the risk
- ensuring that control measures are used, equipment is properly maintained and procedures observed
- monitoring, where necessary, employees' exposure and carrying out an appropriate form of health surveillance
- informing, instructing and training employees about the risks and precautions to be taken.

All employers should consider how COSHH regulations apply to their employees and working environment. For most GPs compliance should be simple and straightforward.

Violence to staff

Violence against doctors and other health workers has been steadily increasing. The HSE is concerned to ensure that all employers take steps to protect staff from violence, this being a corollary of their general obligation to ensure the health and safety of employees.

The Health and Safety Commission's advice emphasizes employers' legal responsibilities and stresses that, where violent incidents can be foreseen, they have a duty to try to safeguard their staff. It also highlights areas in general practice where a few relatively simple measures can reduce the risk of violence. These include:

- rearranging the seating and layout of waiting rooms
- ensuring reception staff can keep an eye on patients and watch for signs of trouble
- incorporating into treatment rooms means of easy access or escape, and alarms or panic buttons to summon help
- designing furniture and fittings so they cannot be used as weapons.

Particular attention should be paid to the risks to staff making home visits by:

- keeping a record of their whereabouts
- setting up procedures for assessing potential or actual risk from patients
- providing information on 'high risk' patients and practice areas.

All staff working in areas where there is known to be a high risk of violence should discuss its causes, learn how to recognize signs of impending attack and develop the skills required to deal with it.

The Health and Safety Commission advises against 'short, largely theoretical courses concerned with why violence and aggression occur'; these will not be sufficient for staff to develop the practical skills and confidence required to handle potentially violent patients.

A plan should be drawn up so that staff are clear about what action they should take in the event of a violent attack.

New health and safety regulations

Six new sets of health and safety at work regulations came into force in 1993. They apply to virtually all kinds of work activity, including general practice. Like existing health and safety law, these new regulations place a duty on employers to protect both employees and other users of the premises.

These new regulations both implement EC directives and update existing UK law, and cover:

- general health and safety management
- work equipment safety
- manual handling of loads
- workplace conditions
- personal protective equipment
- display screen equipment.

Most of the duties laid down are not new; they merely make current health and safety law more explicit. Practices which already comply with the HSW Act and its regulations should have no difficulty with these new regulations. But there are some new approaches, especially in relation to the management of health and safety and the use of VDUs, which practices may have to take into account. This section describes these two sets of regulations.

General health and safety management regulations

These set out general duties aimed at improving health and safety management. If a practice is already thorough in its approach to health and safety, the new regulations should not be problematic.

The new regulations require all employers to:

- assess any risks to the health and safety of employees and anyone else who may be affected by their work. This enables employers to identify any necessary preventive and protective measures. Employers with five or more employees should write their risk assessments down. (This same threshold already applies to the preparation of written health and safety policies)

- make arrangements for implementing the preventive and protective measures that have been identified by the risk assessment: they should cover planning, organization, control, monitoring and review (i.e. the management of health and safety). Again, employers with five or more employees must put these arrangements in writing

- carry out a health surveillance of employees where appropriate

- appoint a competent person (normally an employee) to help devise and apply the protective steps shown to be necessary by the risk assessment

- set up emergency procedures

- give employees information on health and safety matters

- cooperate on health and safety matters with other employers sharing the premises (e.g. the District Health Authority or Health Board)

- make sure employees have adequate health and safety training and are capable enough at their jobs to avoid risk

- give whatever health and safety information is needed by temporary staff to meet their needs.

These regulations also:

- place duties on all employees to follow health and safety instructions and report danger

- extend current health and safety law which requires employers to consult employees' safety representatives and provide facilities for them.

These general duties exist alongside the more specific ones laid down in other health and safety regulations. Of course, this does not mean employers have to do everything twice. For example, if a practice has done a risk assessment to comply with the COSHH Regulations, it need not repeat this exercise to comply with these new general management regulations.

VDU health and safety regulations

Unlike most of the new regulations, the health and safety (display screen equipment) regulations do not replace old legislation, but cover a new area of work activity. Generally, working with VDUs is not a high risk activity, but it can lead to muscular and other physical problems, eye fatigue and mental stress. Problems of this kind can be overcome by good ergonomic design of equipment, furniture, the working environment and the tasks performed.

The regulations apply to those VDUs where there is a 'user', that is an employee who habitually uses it as a significant part of normal work. They cover equipment used for the display of text, numbers and graphics regardless of the display process used.

Employers' duties include:

* assessing VDU workstations and reducing risks which are identified
* making sure workstations satisfy minimum requirements set for the VDU itself, keyboard, desk and chair, working environment and task design, and software
* planning VDU work so that there are breaks or changes in activity
* providing information and training for VDU users.

VDU users are also entitled to appropriate eye and eyesight tests, and to special glasses if these are needed and normal ones cannot be used.

An action list

* Issue a written statement of policy on health and safety to all staff. This is only required if there are five or more staff, but it is advisable to issue one even if fewer staff are employed. It can be included in the employment contract.
* Carry out a risk assessment of any significant hazards in the surgery. If there are five or more employees this assessment should be written down.

- Check any known hazards regularly to see if improvements are needed. (Examples include loose floor coverings, any building works, electrical plugs and equipment.)
- Keep an accident book and copies of the accident report form.
- Maintain and service electrical equipment regularly.
- Decide whether to appoint a member of staff (e.g. the practice manager) as a 'safety officer'.
- Warn patients and visitors by written notices of any hazards on the premises, particularly if building or maintenance work is in progress.
- Review the premises' lease or licence agreement which should state who is responsible for its maintenance and repair.

9 Working in GP and Community Hospitals

Many GPs do some hospital work, usually in a local GP or community hospital. The contracts under which they work are varied and often include informal understandings which reflect long-standing working arrangements. In the past contractual matters have been seriously neglected and GPs have sometimes virtually given their services free of charge to their local community. However, in recent years GPs have expressed increasing disquiet with their contractual arrangements and some practices have sought to improve these; having seen the NHS embrace the market philosophy they themselves are less willing to allow their goodwill be exploited.

It is advisable to exercise great caution in the present NHS climate before taking any steps to change contractual arrangements. Many GPs in these hospital posts have very little security of tenure, particularly if they work only one or two sessions per week. Local NHS management's response to a practice's proposals to improve contractual arrangements may be very different from what is anticipated; in some circumstances management may decide to reduce the level of services in response to a demand for increased pay. In particular, GPs need to know that NHS Trusts can choose to offer local contracts which differ from nationally negotiated agreements and do not necessarily contain the same safeguards in respect of job security or annual pay reviews.

GPs should obtain expert advice before raising any proposal with local hospital management. Otherwise they could find themselves unwittingly taking a precipitous or irrevocable step which prejudices their long-term position. In NHS Trusts, GPs should also contact the local negotiating committee (LNC) which negotiates with Trust management on behalf of medical staff.

How GPs are paid for hospital work

Clinical assistant grade

Even though the term 'clinical assistant' is not to be found anywhere in the hospital medical staff terms and conditions of service, this grade is nevertheless covered by the appointment procedures specified in paragraph 94 of these and also by NHS General Whitley Council agreements. When working as a clinical assistant, a GP should be responsible to a consultant and carry an overriding commitment to the hospital service rather than general practice. Thus GPs need to make arrangements to cover their practice obligations during those periods when working as clinical assistants.

Since 1988 the maximum number of notional half days for which a clinical assistant may be contracted is five, unless the doctor is an unrestricted GP principal where the maximum is nine.

Box 9.1:

Under paragraph 61 of the hospital terms and conditions of service a notional half day (i.e. session) is defined as three and a half hours, including travelling time.

Clinical assistant posts are normally 12-month fixed-term contracts and renewed annually. Any emergency and on call duties should be spelt out clearly in the contract.

Box 9.2: Key features of the clinical assistant grade

- travel expenses payable under certain conditions
- limited security of tenure
- study leave at employer's discretion
- pay related not to number of beds but to time commitment of job
- employee status
- no independent clinical responsibility
- no incremental pay scale

Hospital practitioner grade

Applicants for posts in this grade must be GP principals with:

- at least two years' full time (or equivalent) hospital experience in a relevant specialty

OR

- a relevant specialist diploma and five years' experience as a clinical assistant

OR

- other equivalent experience.

Box 9.3: Key features of the hospital practitioner grade

- study leave entitlement of 30 days in three years
- emergency and on call duties should be specified in the contract
- hospital terms and conditions of service apply
- travel expenses paid in some circumstances
- security of tenure
- incremental pay scale
- no independent clinical responsibility

Each post has to be advertised and its commitment cannot exceed five sessions per week. The qualifications and experience required of a post-holder depend on both the post and the views of local consultants. Hospital practitioners do not have independent clinical responsibility and are therefore supervised by consultants. Hospital doctors' terms and conditions of service apply.

Staff fund arrangements

A staff fund is based on a local GP or community hospital and is made up of both bed fund payments and casualty payments. The distribution of payments (which are superannuable) from this fund is agreed among the local participating doctors attached to the hospital. Only GPs on the local FHSA or Health Board list are appointed to the staff of a GP hospital under the bed fund arrangement, and they are free to organize for themselves how the work is undertaken. As independent clinicians they are accountable to their peers. The calculation of bed fund payments for inpatient GP beds is based on bed occupancy not time spent on the work.

Box 9.4: Key features of staff fund arrangements

- independent clinical responsibility – no consultant supervision
- doctor controls admission, management, administration and discharge
- no sick leave
- no study leave
- no annual leave
- no security of tenure
- no travel and other expenses
- very poorly paid

Casualty payments are paid into the bed fund and form part of it. The clinical assistant scale is used to calculate the size of these payments, but the payments as such are not connected to that grade. There are two kinds of payments: a retention fee and a fee which reflects the number of patient attendances. The fee based on attendance reflects the number of new patient attendances and the clinical assistant scale is normally used as an analogue for the rate of payments though this may vary locally.

Typically a given number of new attendances draws one clinical assistant session payment into the bed fund. Although the arrangements for casualty payments do not necessarily require GPs to see all patients when they first attend, each patient should be seen by a doctor at some stage. Nurses may treat minor problems, seeking advice and assistance from GPs as necessary. However, a GP must be available to attend immediately if required.

The content of a contract for hospital services

The contract should state to which consultant the GP is clinically responsible. If supervised by a consultant, the post should normally be graded as either clinical assistant or hospital practitioner; the latter may be preferred because it has greater security of tenure and is more highly paid. Contracts for both grades should specify hours of work; however, it should be noted that although it is comparatively easy to calculate sessional payments for routine work it is usually more difficult to do so for out-of-hours work.

The hours during which casualty work is to be covered must be clearly specified; some GPs with surgeries on the same site as a GP hospital have found that between 9 a.m. and 5 p.m. they receive no pay for casualty work because health authorities mistakenly consider it to be part of general medical services.

Box 9.5: Contract checklist

The contract should include:

- name of employing authority
- date employment commences and any previous employment which may count towards continuity
- place of work
- job description
- hours of work
- superannuation
- remuneration
- annual leave
- study leave
- maternity leave
- sick leave
- definition of clinical responsibility
- substitution and deputizing arrangements
- medical indemnity
- period of notice of termination
- disciplinary procedure
- grievance procedure
- reference to the terms and conditions of service for hospital medical and dental staff, as appropriate.

10 Flexible and Part-time Working in General Practice

> **Where to obtain advice and assistance**
>
> BMA members can obtain expert advice and assistance on all contractual problems from their local BMA office. FHSAs are also an important source of advice. The BMA has published guidance on contracts for GP salaried assistants which includes a model contract of employment.
>
> Further reading includes *Making Sense of Partnerships*, Radcliffe Medical Press and *Making Sense of the Red Book, second edition*, Radcliffe Medical Press.

The main opportunities for flexible and part-time working in general practice are:

- as a principal, particularly part-time and job sharing GPs
- as a restricted services principal
- as a part-time salaried employee – often termed an assistant
- as a member of the doctors' retainer scheme
- as an associate
- as a locum.

Although there are important statutory regulations and employment law governing these flexible and part-time arrangements, the actual contractual terms are matters to be agreed between the practice and the doctor. This latter point is important and needs to be stressed; much of the advice provided below is drawn from the BMA's recommendations relating to fair and reasonable contractual terms, but cannot be regarded as mandatory.

Part-time working as a GP principal

Five options of availability

The GP's terms of service provide five options of availability to patients. These arrangements do not alter a GP's basic responsibility to ensure that, either personally or through a deputy, general medical services are provided for patients throughout each and every day that his or her name is included on an FHSA or Health Board list.

Full-time over five days

This option requires a GP to be normally available for not less than 26 hours spread over five days each week, for 42 weeks in any 12-month period.

Full-time over four days

This second option allows a GP to be normally available for not less than 26 hours spread over four days each week for 42 weeks in any 12-month period. Doctors may apply for this option if they are involved in health-related activities, which are defined in the NHS regulations as those connected with:

• organization of the medical profession or training of its members
• providing medical care or treatment
• improving quality of care or treatment
• administering general medical services.

FHSAs and Health Boards should be guided by the illustrative list of these activities shown in Box 10.1.

Three-quarter time

A three quarter time contract allows a GP to be normally available for not less than 19 hours each week on days to be agreed with the FHSA or Health Board, for 42 weeks each year. This option is only available to GPs in a partnership with at least one full-time practitioner.

Half-time

A half time GP normally has to be available for not less than 13 hours each week on days to be agreed with the FHSA or Health Board, for

---

Box 10.1: Health related activities

- appointments concerned with medical education or training; for example, regional adviser, course organizer or an academic appointment

- medical appointments within the health service other than in relation to the provision of general medical services; for example, hospital appointments (such as hospital practitioner, clinical assistant and GP hospital posts) and also health service management and advisory posts, including health authority, FHSA and Health Board duties

- medical appointments made under the Crown, with Government departments or agencies, or public or local authorities; for example, medical work for the police or prison service

- appointments concerning the regulation of the medical profession or the MPC; for example, General Medical Council (GMC) appointments, membership of the national GMSCs (including Welsh, Scottish and Northern Ireland GMSCs) or the Royal College of General Practitioners (RCGP) at national level, or service on an LMC

---

42 weeks each year. This option is only available to GPs in a partnership with at least one full-time practitioner.

Job sharing

This enables a joint application by doctors in a partnership which includes both of them. Together they must be normally available for not less than 26 hours over five days each week for 42 weeks each year. The two doctors should decide how the 26 hours are to be divided.

Non-availability

Each of the above options requires the GP to be normally available for 42 weeks in any 12-month period. Throughout the 42 weeks but outside approved hours and during the remaining 10 weeks, a GP is free to make reasonable arrangement with a partner or a deputy for the care of patients.

Box 10.2: Minimum profit shares of part-timers

Full-time principals	minimum share is one-third of that of partner with the greatest share
Three-quarter time principals	minimum share is one-quarter of that of partner with the greatest share
Half-time principals	minimum share is one-fifth of that of partner with the greatest share
Job sharers	minimum joint share is one-third of that of partner with greatest share

(These minimum profit shares apply only to the NHS component of the partnership profits. Income from work outside NHS general practice is excluded from the calculation.)

Profit share and part-time partners

Under NHS regulations, for the FHSA or Health Board to recognize GPs as partners, it must be satisfied that they discharge the duties and exercise the powers of principals in the partnership and are entitled to a profit share based on one of the options in Box 10.2.

Each partnership must decide for itself how to run its business. But if any partner's share is grossly out of line with his or her contribution to the practice's workload, a concealed sale of goodwill may be deemed to have taken place.

Discrimination

It is unlawful for a partnership of two or more partners to discriminate on grounds of sex or marital status, and for a partnership of six ore more partners to discriminate on grounds of colour, race, nationality (including citizenship) or ethnic or national origins:

- when appointing a new partner
- in the terms on which the new partner is offered a partnership
- by refusing, or deliberately neglecting to offer a partnership

and where someone is already a partner:

- in the way he or she is afforded access to any benefits, facilities or services
- by refusing, or deliberately neglecting, to afford access to those benefits, facilities and services
- by dismissing the partner, or treating him or her unfavourably in any other way.

Maternity leave

As self-employed independent contractors women GP principals do not enjoy the employment rights relating to pregnancy and childbirth that apply to women employees. Thus partnerships are free to make their own arrangements for an individual partner's maternity leave. (*See* Box 10.3 for an outline of some recommended maternity leave arrangements for partnerships.)

There are various arrangements for paying locums employed during prolonged absences such as those arising from sickness or maternity leave. A simple method is for the absent partner to pay all the locum expenses. However, it is increasingly common for the first few weeks of locum expenses to be paid by the whole partnership.

A partnership will be infringing the Sex Discrimination Act 1976 if a pregnant partner is treated less favourably than a male partner with a distinctly male incapacity. Therefore a partner on maternity leave should not have to meet the full cost of a locum unless this arrangement also applies to sick leave.

A woman GP who provides unrestricted general medical services and is paid a basic practice allowance can claim additional payments for a locum actually engaged during absences due to pregnancy and childbirth. These payments are similar to those paid during sickness, but for maternity there are no list size criteria. The payments are available for a maximum period of 13 weeks. These additional payments from the FHSA or Health Board should be paid to the absent partner if she is responsible for locum expenses. (Eligibility for additional payments during sickness depend on the average number of patients that the remaining GPs have to care for during the absence.)

The question of how long a partnership or individual partner pays locum expenses needs to be decided in relation to the arrangements for insurance cover for income protection and/or locum expenses.

Partnership agreements

As well as the minimum share of the profits referred to above, a doctor who is in partnership must discharge the duties and exercise the powers of a principal in the running of the partnership; irrespective of whether he or she is a part-time, job-sharing or full time principal.

Box 10.3: Recommended arrangements for maternity leave

- 14 weeks absence should be regarded as a minimum entitlement and the pregnant partner should have the right to determine for herself when the period of absence should start, in consultation with her own GP

- the practice should consider the question of funding the cost of a locum to cover the actual workload of the pregnant partner, not merely her hours of availability

- the partnership should agree on a maximum period of absence following which a partner's failure to return to work may justify compulsory expulsion

- the exercise of a partner's right to maternity leave should not abolish her entitlement to *pro rata* holiday and sickness leave

- where this seems appropriate the partnership agreement should specify leave arrangements for adoption

A partnership agreement which provides for maternity leave on terms which are less advantageous than sick leave could be construed as evidence of indirect sex discrimination.

Working as a restricted services principal

The 'restricted services principal' provides general medical services which are limited to:

- child health surveillance services

- contraceptive services
- maternity medical services
- minor surgery services
- or any combination of these.

This is quite distinct from the 'restricted list principal' who cares for a restricted category of patients connected with a particular establishment or organization.

In general, a restricted services principal is eligible to only receive:

- those fees related to the particular service being provided
- discretionary payments under the rent and rates scheme and practice staff scheme.

Restricted principals providing maternity, contraceptive or child health surveillance services are also eligible to receive modified payments under the sickness and confinement schemes; but those providing only minor surgery services are not.

Doctors applying to become restricted principals for the minor surgery and child health surveillance lists will be approved only if they work either in a group with one or more principals or as an assistant or deputy of a principal who is on the relevant list. A restricted services principal must satisfy the specific criteria for entry to the relevant special list.

Working as a salaried assistant

The GP's terms of service require the FHSA or Health Board to be told when an assistant is being employed. The GP is not allowed to employ one or more assistants for more than three months in any 12-month period without FHSA or Health Board consent, irrespective of whether the assistant's employment qualifies for the assistant's allowance.

GPs may employ assistants at their own expense; they are eligible for additional payments (the assistant's allowance) only if the criteria in Red Book paragraphs 18.1–18.6 are satisfied.

GPs are also eligible for additional payments for employing a locum to cover an assistant's absence because of sickness or maternity, if the assistant continues to be paid full salary during the period of absence.

Assistants should agree with their employing practices written contracts and job descriptions. Every employer is required to issue a written statement of the main terms of employment to any employee working at least eight hours per week within two months of starting work.

Anyone considering working as an assistant may find the following check-list a helpful guide to those subjects which should be covered by an employment contract:

- pay including provision for annual review
- hours of work including any flexibility requirement
- holiday leave and pay entitlement
- sick leave and pay entitlement
- maternity leave and pay entitlement
- pensions arrangements
- notice of termination of contract
- grievance procedures
- arrangements for motoring expenses, medical defence organization and other professional subscriptions.

In addition, there should be an agreed job description which describes the post's responsibilities and duties. Box 10.4 summarizes the employment rights of part-timers and whole-timers.

GP assistant's pay

It is not possible to specify a particular rate of pay or formula for determining pay which can suit all circumstances; ultimately a GP assistant's salary has to reflect the circumstances of the appointment: relevant factors include previous experience, hours of work, job content and the income of the practice. The GMSC has suggested two possible ways of determining a GP assistant's salary:

- a specific rate of pay such as a salary which may be linked to some external comparator
- a formula which relates pay to the income of the practice.

Whichever is used, the actual salary must take account of both the practice's financial circumstances and the nature of the post itself.

The option of basing an assistant's salary on a specific rate of pay has the advantage of simplicity (possible analogues include the NHS clinical assistant and hospital practitioner grades). The actual pay rate could take account of various factors including:

- previous experience
- hours of work

Box 10.4: Part-timers' employment rights

Minimum weekly hours and length of service required to qualify for statutory employment rights. At the time of writing an important ruling by the House of Lords will require the Government to extend unfair dismissal and redundancy rights to include anyone with two years' service who works eight hours a week or more. This table presupposes that the Government has enacted amending employment legislation to implement the House of Lords' ruling.

Employment right	under eight hours	eight hours or more
Unfair dismissal (general)	no right	two years' service
Unfair dismissal (inadmissible reasons)	unrestricted	unrestricted
Notice of dismissal	no right	one month's service
Written reason for dismissal[a]	no right	two years' service
Redundancy pay	no right	two years' service
Right to return after maternity absence (up to 29 weeks after childbirth)	no right	two years' service
Maternity leave (14 weeks)[b]	unrestricted	unrestricted
Statutory maternity pay[c]	no right	six months' service (see footnote)
Written particulars	no right	two months' service
Guaranteed pay	no right	two years' service
Time off for union duties	no right	unrestricted
Equal pay	unrestricted	unrestricted
Sex discrimination	unrestricted	unrestricted
Race discrimination	unrestricted	unrestricted
Ante-natal leave	unrestricted	unrestricted

[a] If a woman is pregnant or taking maternity leave when dismissed, the right to written reasons is unrestricted by service requirements.
[b] Various new maternity rights introduced by the Trade Union Reform and Employment Rights Act 1993 come into force in October 1994. A woman is eligible to take 40 weeks' maternity leave if she works at least 16 hours a week and has at least 2 years' service (or between eight and 16 hours and five years' service).
[c] SMP is paid after six months; entitlement to higher rate SMP (90 percent of earnings) depends on length of service and hours worked per week.

- out-of-hours commitment
- duties performed.

Some practices may wish to use a fairly complex formula to calculate relative workloads of both partners and salaried assistants.

The other option, where an assistant's salary is based on a percentage of practice profits, also needs to take account of the factors listed above. It is hard to specify a percentage of parity to suit all circumstances; the GMSC has suggested that a minimum 70–75 per cent of parity should be a fair basis for calculating the salary for a full time GP assistant who does the whole range of general medical service duties (including the practice's out-of-hours commitment) but does not share the managerial responsibilities of the employing partners.

The doctors' retainer scheme

The scheme helps doctors under the age of 55 years who work not more than one day a week to keep in touch with medicine so that they can return to the NHS when circumstances permit. They are offered the opportunity of doing a small amount of paid professional work and to attend postgraduate medical education sessions; in return, scheme members are paid a retainer to help meet expenses. Some 600 GPs are currently in the scheme.

A doctor joining the scheme agrees to:

- maintain GMC registration and membership of a medical defence organization
- attend at least seven educational sessions a year, which may be arranged to fit in with family responsibilities
- take a professional journal such as the *British Medical Journal*
- work at least one half-day a month and be prepared to take on more work, up to maximum of one day a week (if asked to do so) if this does not interfere with family commitments.

How the scheme is organized

Regional Health Authorities have been responsible for the general administration of the scheme; they accept new members and pay the annual retainer fee. Professional advice and guidance about educational facilities are provided by clinical tutors who should discuss career prospects with scheme members and advise them on local postgraduate activities. Clinical tutors review progress with scheme members at least annually. Educational sessions attended by members should be relevant to their current work and their eventual return to regular practice.

Scheme members may work in various fields; including hospitals, general practice, public health medicine and community health services. The employer is responsible for arranging and paying for work done. Membership is on a year by year basis and continues automatically for a whole year even if a member's professional commitments increase to more than one day a week.

The retainer fee and income tax

The retainer fee should be treated as earned income and taxed under Schedule E; but it is not liable for superannuation or NI contributions. After deducting allowable expenses, the remaining balance will attract any personal income tax relief to which the doctor is entitled; these expenses are those incurred wholly exclusively, and necessarily, in the performance of professional duties; for example, the annual GMC retention fee and subscriptions to professional bodies, such as a medical defence organization and the BMA. (Subscription rates to medical defence organizations and the BMA are reduced for doctors with this level of income.)

Other fees: superannuation and income tax

Although fees paid by the practice for work done under the scheme are liable to income tax and class 1 NI contributions, they are not superannuable even if the retainee is described as an assistant. However, if a doctor already has two or more years service with the NHS Pension Scheme his or her accrued benefits can be preserved. If total service is less than this, these benefits may be lost after a 12-month break in service; the doctor can prevent this by working at least one day in each 12-month period in superannuable employment. Alternatively if none of the work undertaken in connection with the scheme is superannuable (e.g. working as a GP assistant) a doctor may apply to the NHS Pensions Agency at the Department of Health, 200–220 Broadway, Fleetwood, Lancs FY7 8LG, for employment under the scheme to be 'approved' for superannuation purposes, in order to avoid incurring a disqualifying break in service of 12 months or more.

Working as an associate

The Associate scheme enables single-handed isolated GPs to employ an associate. This allows them regular time off and training, in circumstances where continuous duty is an otherwise inescapable feature of their practice. Normally an associate is employed by two practices; although three may sometimes be appropriate. (GPs with assistants are ineligible for the scheme.)

Those GPs who participate in this scheme, and are also paid inducement payments, are no longer entitled to claim locum expenses, other than in the most exceptional circumstances.

Box 10.5 explains how the scheme has been modified to take account of the special geographical circumstances of remote areas of Scotland.

Box 10.5: Special Scottish circumstances

Particular geographical difficulties, especially in the highlands and islands, may mean that it is impractical for two or three neighbouring principals to employ an associate. In these circumstances, Health Boards can organize a scheme if asked to do so by GPs.

GPs in very isolated areas, where groupings of two or three eligible principals are difficult if not impossible to arrange, can ask their Health Board to act as the paying agent on their behalf and to employ a suitably qualified associate. Though the Board appoints, pays and deploys these associates, responsibility for them under the terms of service remains with the principal. In these circumstances, where the Board only acts solely as the agent, GPs should ensure that they are adequately represented on the selection panel appointed by the Board to recruit associates.

To qualify for this allowance a GP must be single-handed (including job sharers) and:

• in receipt of rural practice payments

OR

• the sole practitioner on an island

AND ALSO

• in receipt of an inducement payment

OR

- practising more than 10 miles (measured along the most practicable route) from the nearest GP's main surgery or nearest district general hospital.

Doctors employed as associates must satisfy vocational training regulations and be eligible to apply to join an FHSA or Health Board list, but whilst holding this appointment must not be included on such a list.

Associates undertake all GP work and their employing GPs are responsible for their actions including any breach of the terms of service. The associate scheme is broadly similar to the GP trainee scheme; the associate doctor has the same contractual relationship with the GP employer, the same accountability arrangements and the same tax status as a trainee does.

Because a GP principal is accountable for the activities of an associate, he or she should employ someone with the necessary skills and aptitude to be able to practise in social and professional isolation. This scheme may become a step in the career structure, offering a route to obtaining an isolated or inducement practice. A short-term 'apprenticeship' as an associate can enable a younger doctor to assess his or her own suitability for this type of practice.

The employing practice decides the associate's salary, but the amount reimbursed directly by the FHSA or Health Board will be on the associate scale of payments as set annually by the Review Body. Other reimbursements include a car allowance, telephone expenses, removal expenses, the cost of medical defence organization subscriptions, the employer's NI contributions and other expenses similar to those covered by the GP trainee practitioner scheme. An associate may receive the postgraduate education allowance and time spent as an associate will count towards seniority payments in the same way as for GP assistants. Where two or three GPs jointly employ an associate, one of them has to be responsible to the FHSA or Health Board for administering salary, allowances and tax deductions.

The FHSA or Health Board has to be satisfied that the arrangements ensure continuity of care for patients, equitable and regular time off for both the GPs and the associate, that they cover the annual and postgraduate study leave, and that the associate is employed on a full time basis. (In England and Wales the FHSA can ask to see the associate's contract of employment.)

What an associate does

It is for the employing doctors to determine how an associate is deployed between the participating practices. However, doctors in isolated areas often have small lists of a few hundred patients so it is inappropriate for a principal to use the associate as simply an extra pair of hands; it is not the practice's workload that should need relieving but the unremitting on-call commitment. Most participating GPs will wish to be relieved of their practice responsibilities on a regular basis (probably for at least a week at a time) to compensate for the difficulties of ferry travel or long road journeys when leaving the practice area for a worthwhile break. At other times (e.g. school holidays) it should be possible to arrange a sustained break whilst staying in their own area knowing that time with their families will not be disrupted by practice commitments. It should be re-membered that any practice arrangements will be subject to disruption in the event of sickness or maternity leave involving either practitioner or associate. When this occurs, balancing periods of leave or extra duty may be required to ensure equity.

Working as a locum

Locums in general practice can work long term or short term, part-time or full-time to cover, for example, a principal's absence on maternity or study leave, extended leave of absence or illness, or to cover a period before a new partner is appointed. Terms of employment vary, as does the existence of a contract of employment. Some locums also work for deputizing services on a sessional basis.

Doctors may find locum employment advantageous, say, following vocational training when they may want experience in various practices before becoming a principal. Disadvantages may include poor job satis-faction, especially when there is no opportunity for continuity of patient care, lack of a proper contract of employment, poor pay and inadequate continuing medical education. Only long-term locums are eligible to claim Section 63 expenses for travel and subsistence to attend educational courses. Expenses are not normally reimbursed for locums on short-term contracts. The BMA can advise members on appropriate fees for locum work.

11 Part-time Medical Work Outside the NHS

Although there are no official data on the amount of non-NHS work GPs undertake, unpublished data and anecdotal evidence suggest that the totality of GPs' earnings from this source amounts on average to barely one or two per cent of their gross NHS income. Thus the total amount of these earnings is probably much smaller than is generally assumed. The extent of this work within general practice is often overestimated, because a small minority of practices who are heavily and enthusiastically involved in it have given wide publicity to its considerable potential income.

The main sources of GP earnings outside the NHS are:

- a wide range of miscellaneous fees paid for various part-time medical services
- private general practice
- work in occupational health.

Non-NHS medical work

GPs may charge fees for a range of non-NHS work; they include fees for local or central government work, reports or certificates for their patients or third parties, and cremation certificates. Nevertheless, it needs to be remembered that GPs are prohibited by their NHS contracts from charging fees in certain specific circumstances (*see* Box 3.10, Chapter 3).

The level of fees that may be charged depends on whom the work is being carried out for and how the level is determined. The BMA divides these fees into four main categories (designated A, B, C and D) according to how they are determined (*see* Box 11.1).

Box 11.1: BMA categories of fees

Category A	fees prescribed by statute
Category B	fee negotiated nationally by the BMA with Government departments, local authorities and other employers
Category C	fees negotiated nationally with representative bodies
Category D	fee suggested by the BMA

The BMA publishes some 35 separate fee guides (*see* Box 11.2 below); each describes the level of fees applying to a particular area of work and the circumstances in which they may be paid; these cover several hundred individual fees and help to ensure GPs are paid correctly for their non-NHS services.

The BMA considers that if an official body commissions a medical examination, report or certificate for which a GP may charge a fee, the commissioning body should be liable to pay it.

Box 11.2: Fees for part-time medical services

List of BMA fees guides (fees supplements: 'FSs')

FS1- Mileage, subsistence and financial loss allowances

FS2- Central Government departments: general schedule

FS3- Central Government departments: DH and DSS
      Appendix A – fees negotiated by the BMA
      Appendix B – fees and allowances laid down by
      HM Treasury

FS4- Central Government departments – Ministry of Defence

FS5- Central Government departments – Employment Service Division

FS6- Central Government departments – Department of Transport

FS7- Central Government departments – Home Office and Scottish Home and
      Health Department (Prison)

FS8- Central Government departments – Home Office (Criminal Injuries
      Compensation Board)

FS9- Central Government departments – Lord Chancellor's Department

FS10- Central Government departments – Health and Safety Executive
      Employment Medical Advisory Service (EMAS)

FS11- HSE

FS12- National Society for the Prevention of Cruelty to Children

FS13- Voluntary aid societies

FS14- British Coal

FS15- Life assurance reports

FS16- Emergency treatment at road traffic accidents

FS17- Miscellaneous fees in the NHS

FS18- Not applicable to general practice

FS19- Family planning clinics

FS20- Dental anaesthetics

FS21- Sessional work in community health service

FS22- Medical examinations of prospective NHS employees

FS23 - Work under the collaborative arrangements for local authorities: for
       example, community care assessments

FS24 - Visiting medical officers to establishments maintained by local authorities

FS25 - Doctors assisting local authorities

FS26 - Medical referees at crematoria

FS27 - Police surgeons

FS28 - Home office appointed pathologists

FS29 - Coroners' analytical work

FS30 - Coroners' work reports

FS31 - Coroners' work: post mortem examinations and attendance at inquests

FS32 - Blood tests (evidence of paternity) regulations

FS33 - Medico-legal fees and allowances
       Appendix A – fees paid by the Crown Prosecution Service
       Appendix B – fees paid out of public funds (Legal Aid Board)
       Appendix C – fees suggested by the BMA

FS34 - Where no agreement applies

Category A: statutory fees

Typical examples are those fees paid for post mortem examinations requested by a coroner and for emergency treatment at road traffic accidents. They are always paid strictly according to the conditions stipulated in the relevant legislation. Box 11.3 lists the main types of fees in this category.

Category B: fees negotiated with central government departments and public sector employers

These fees guides/supplements are available to BMA members only and are free of charge. Members should ask their local office for copies.

These are traditionally linked to Review Body recommendations; typical examples include fees for medical boards and part-time services for health authorities and police authorities. They are paid by the Government department or employer which negotiated the fee. Boxes 11.4 and 11.5 summarize the main fees in this category. At the time of writing the profession is in dispute with the Government because it has deliberately breached an agreement to increase these fees.

Category C: fees negotiated with representative organizations

Typical examples are fees for life assurance reports, and work for voluntary and charitable societies. The BMA's negotiated fees apply to only those organizations which are members of the national representative body; for example, life assurance report fees are only binding on member companies of the British Association of Life Insurers. Box 11.6 lists the main fees in this category.

Category D: recommended fees

This category includes all those fees not determined by negotiation or statute; they are left to be agreed between the GP and the party concerned. The extensive list of the many and varied types in Box 11.7 is provided as a reminder of private service for which GPs may charge patients. GPs are often reticent about charging NHS patients for non-NHS services and patients are correspondingly reluctant to pay for them. In a publicly funded service which is still permeated by the non-pecuniary ethos, GPs and patients are unaccustomed to monetary transactions. Each practice will obviously determine its own policy on charging patients for this work; a determined effort may have to be made to overcome any inhibitions

Box 11.3: Category A: statutory fees and fees determined by government departments

- fees payable for coroners' work, post mortem examinations and attendances at inquests (FS31)
- fees for blood tests and reports relating to evidence of paternity (FS32)
- allowances to witnesses to fact in criminal cases for both written medical reports and attendance at court (FS33)
- emergency treatment at road traffic accidents (FS16)
- examinations under the Factories Acts and health and safety at work legislation (FS11)
- medical examinations required under the diving regulations (FS6)
- aviation medical fees
- dental anaesthetic fees (FS20)
- seafarers' statutory medical examinations

Box 11.4: Category B: fees for work done for central government departments

Range of fees for various procedures including:

- medical examinations and reports
- medical attendance on non-NHS patients
- immunizations and vaccinations not covered by NHS
- regular attendance at Government establishments
- membership of medical boards, tribunals etc.

Ministry of Defence (FS4)

- work as GPs
- service recruits' examinations
- temporary locums for armed forces medical officers
- lectures to medical officers
- attendance on service personnel on leave from their units

continued opposite

Box 11.4: *continued*

Employment Service Division (FS5)

- disablement advisory committees panels

Department of Transport (FS6)

- extract from medical records or completing DVLA question-naires
- DVLA diagnostic tests

DSS (FS3)

- fees for various reports required for pension and other purposes
- part-time referee for the Benefits Agency medical service
- membership of various tribunals

HSE (FS11)

- extracts from records plus opinion

Home Office (Prison Service) (FS7)

- part-time prison medical officers (agreed directly with the Home Office (Prison Service)

about introducing the cash nexus into patient-doctor relations, and to inform patients of which NHS service they can legitimately expect to receive free of charge, and for which non-NHS services they can properly be charged.

Deciding what to charge

GPs should clarify whether they are entitled to charge a fee before agreeing to provide a service. If it is clear that a fee may be charged, the next question that has to be answered is for whom is the medical service being provided. This is crucial because its answer determines both the level of fee and who should pay it. Whether or not a fee may be charged is determined by either parliamentary statute or the GP's terms of service. It is advisable to forewarn patients of any charge before undertaking the

Box 11.5: Category B: fees for medical services for local and health authorities

- work under the collaborative arrangements: although the service is provided by a GP for a local authority on behalf of a health authority (on part-time sessional or item of service basis), the body requesting the work should ensure that the doctor is paid although its payment is ultimately the responsibility of the health authority (FS23). Examples of this work include:
  - notifying a case of notifiable disease or food poisoning
  - medical examinations and reports for adoption and fostering
  - medical examination of children in care
  - visiting medical officers to establishments maintained by local authorities
  - medical referees at crematoria
  - assessment for community care purposes
- medical examinations of prospective NHS employees (FS22)
- medical examinations of employees and prospective employees of local authorities (FS25)
- police surgeons' fees (FS27)

Box 11.6: Category C: fees for private sector work

- fees for life assurance reports (FS15)
- HIV testing for life assurance purposes (FS34)
- voluntary aid societies (e.g. British Red Cross Society, St John Ambulance Association) (FS13)
- NSPCC (FS12)
- British Coal (FS14)

work. Hopefully this should avoid some of the embarrassment that can arise in NHS general practice when charges are being made for non-NHS services. Some practices find it helpful to have a notice about this in the waiting room.

GPs are obliged under paragraph 13 of their terms of service to provide patients with "all necessary and appropriate personal medical services of the type usually provided by general practitioners" for which they are not permitted to ask or accept, any payment (*see* paragraph 37) except if this is specifically allowed in the terms of service (*see* paragraph 38). A full list of services for which an NHS patient may be charged is in Box 3.10 (chapter 3). Although some certificates may be charged for, NHS GPs are obliged under their terms of service to provide the certificates specified in Box 3.9 (chapter 3) free of charge, including those supporting social security benefit claims.

Private general practice

There is no limit on the amount of private practice NHS GPs may under-take provided they fulfil their NHS commitment. If staff or premises, which are directly reimbursed for NHS purposes, are used and a practice's private practice income is more than 10 per cent of total practice receipts, these NHS reimbursements will be abated. Under no circumstances, except those referred to above which are permitted under their terms of service, can GPs charge a fee to their own NHS patients.

The actual amount of private practice undertaken by NHS GPs as a whole is very small; only a small minority of practices are likely to have a significant number of private patients. Typically NHS GPs accept private patients only on request; they do not advertise for patients, though they are now free to do so subject to the rules laid down by the General Medical Council.

An NHS GP cannot treat a patient both privately and on the NHS concurrently. This is because GPs' terms of service prohibit them from accepting any payment from patients for whose treatment they are respon-sible under their NHS contract, unless such payments are specifically authorized. This restriction on receiving payments extends to patients registered with the GP's partners. Some patients have both an NHS GP and a private GP from a different practice.

A private GP may agree to be 'on call' for private patients but is not obliged to do so unless the contract with the patient specifically includes an out-of-hours service. The NHS out-of-hours contractual obligation does not apply to the private sector.

Box 11.7: Category D: fees suggested by the BMA for various types of private work

(Most of these fees are covered by FS34)

- holiday insurance certificate
- blood test (not involving disputed paternity)
- court of protection medical certificates
- cervical cytology (non-NHS)
- private medical consultations
- copying medical notes
- comprehensive medical examinations and reports
- fitness to attend court as a witness
- cremation forms B and C
- removal of a pacemaker following death
- pre-employment examinations
- reports requested by employers
- private sickness absence certificates for school or work
- motor insurance certificates of fitness
- accident and sickness insurance certificates
- validation of provident association claim form
- school fees insurance
- fitness for higher education
- fitness to participate in a sport
- freedom from infection certificate
- vaccination and immunization
- attendances at police stations not covered by NHS fee at patient's request
- family planning
- lecture fees
- non-NHS minor surgery
- seatbelt exemption certificates
- prescriptions for drugs required in overseas travel
- reports for drug companies

continued opposite

Box 11.7: *continued*

- race meetings and sporting activities
- private nursing homes
- data protection legislation: search of records
- access to medical records: copying fee
- reports on prospective subscribers to health insurance
- non-medical services (e.g. passport signing)
- payments to deputizing doctors
- radio and TV broadcasts
- fees for involvement in legal work (i.e. professional witnesses and expert witnesses)

Box 11.8: Services for which fees may not be charged

Death certificates

In England and Wales, the registered medical practitioner who was in attendance upon the deceased during his or her last illness must deliver a death certificate, stating to the best of his or her knowledge and belief, the cause of death to the local registrar forthwith, and he or she may not charge a fee for this service. Failure to deliver the certificate 'without reasonable excuse' is punishable on summary conviction with a fine. He or she must also hand the person designated as 'qualified informant' the outer detachable part of the certificate form entitled 'Notice to Informant', duly completed.

Stillbirth certificates

Any registered medical practitioner who was present at the birth or examined the body of a stillborn child must, upon a request from the 'qualified informant', give a certificate stating that the child was not born alive, and, where possible, stating to the best of his or her knowledge and belief the cause of death and estimated duration of the pregnancy.

continued overleaf

Box 11.8: *continued*

GPs under contract to FHSA (Health Board in Scotland)

The items for which doctors may not make charges are listed in Schedule 2 (term of service for doctors) of the NHS (General Medical Services) Regulations 1992 (Statutory Instrument No 635) as amended. In Scotland they are listed in Schedule 1 of The NHS (General Medical and Pharmaceutical Services) (Scotland) Regulations 1974 (Statutory Instrument No 506) as amended. Subsequent amendments are incorporated into the following:

(i)   England and Wales   Paragraphs 38–42 of the England and Wales Schedule

(ii) Scotland   Paragraph 20 of the Scottish Schedule.

NHS GPs must only provide an NHS prescription (FP10) to their NHS patients; they cannot prescribe an NHS prescription for their private patients.

Many NHS GPs treat their private patients on the same or a very similar basis to their NHS patients; both surgery and domiciliary consultations are arranged to fit in with their NHS commitments.

Private general practice is based on a personal contract between the doctor and patient. For some years the provident associations have not shown any interest in offering insurance schemes to cover the costs of private general practice, although some insurance companies have recently expressed an interest in such policies.

There is one aspect of general practice which merits further clarification, namely the treatment of overseas visitors. The Health Department circular which governs these matters (HN(FP)(84)7) states that, apart from imme-diately necessary (i.e. emergency) treatment, the NHS GP has unrestricted discretion as to whether to treat a non-EC visitor as a temporary resident and NHS patient, or as a wholly private patient. The health circular makes it clear that many non-EC visitors expect to pay for medical treatment and GPs will not be committing any offence or breach of their terms of service if they offer to treat overseas visitors privately on whatever terms are mutually agreed. However, most visitors from other EC countries have some entitlement under EC regulations to use the NHS, including GP services. Their entitlement varies according to their employment and/or visitor status. For most purposes it is best to assume they (together with nationals from non EC or European Economic Area states who have signed the European Social Charter) are entitled to free NHS treatment, except in the case of treatment which they have specifically come to the UK to obtain.

The circular also states that if no local NHS GP is willing to treat the non-EC visitor on an NHS basis, he or she can apply to the FHSA to be assigned to the list of a local GP. The GP to whom the patient is assigned is obliged to provide NHS general medical services free of charge for the minimum number of days as specified in the NHS terms of service. There is, however, a major difference between primary and secondary care. Even if an overseas visitor receives NHS general medical services, access to NHS secondary care entirely depends upon residency status and country of origin.

Occupational health

Although many doctors working in this specialty hold full-time salaried posts in large commercial and industrial organizations, there are also many part-time occupational physicians, most of whom are GPs. Some small firms prefer to employ a local doctor on a part-time sessional basis and GPs are ideally suited to fill these posts, although many firms have no occupational health service at all.

The BMA's Occupational Health Committee publishes suggested salary ranges for full and part-time occupational physician posts and annualized salaries based on one hour, two hours or one session (three and a half hours) per week. These scales are included in a BMA booklet *The Occupational Physician* which also provides guidance on managing occupational health departments, and notes on health and safety in the workplace. These scales take account of the doctor's qualifications in occupational medicine (e.g. AFOM or DIH), previous relevant experience and level of responsibility. Thus GPs who are members or fellows of the Faculty of Occupational Medicine and are accredited specialists and/or have considerable experience should start at relatively higher salaries. The scales are based on the assumption that the GP does not benefit from paid annual leave or membership of the firm's superannuation scheme.

An occupational physician is in a somewhat unusual position in relation to the organization's workforce in that there may be a danger that the normal rules governing medical ethics and confidentiality conflict with his or her responsibility to the organization's management. Guidance on how to handle these potentially conflicting responsibilities is provided in two BMA publications *The Occupational Physician* and *Medical Ethics Today: its philosophy and practice.*

Box 11.9: The duties of an occupational physician are of two main kinds:

- assessing and moderating the effects of health on an individual's capacity to work, including:
  - advising employers on such matters as pre-employment and annual medical examinations
  - immediately treating clinical emergencies at the place of work
  - examining and monitoring employees returning to work after prolonged sickness absence
  - advising management on health surveillance and screening
- assessing and moderating the effects of work on an individual's health which includes:
  - providing first aid services
  - examining and supervising medically those employees exposed to special hazards
  - advising management on the working environment, health risks, safety hazards and statutory requirements relating to health and safety at the workplace
  - supervising the hygiene of staff facilities, especially kitchens, canteens etc
  - educating the staff on matters pertaining to health, fitness and hygiene.

Police surgeon work

The remuneration of police surgeons (which is classified as category B work) consists of a flat rate 'availability fee' plus a two-tier item of service fee; the fee for the first case being higher than for subsequent cases on the same call-out. These item of service fees are also payable if a doctor who is not a contracted police surgeon agrees to undertake the police visit. The fees are jointly negotiated by the BMA and the local government employers' organization, and apply throughout Great Britain.

The 'availability fee' is a standard flat rate payment and not dependent on fee income. It may be supplemented by a further payment if the doctor has a relevant qualification (eg the diploma of medical jurisprudence or some other recognized qualification in forensic medicine) or has had 15 years' continuous service as a police surgeon (or deputy), normally with the same police force.

The item of service fees are paid when a doctor attends in response to a call from the police; they vary according to:

- when the call-out occurred
- length of time involved
- type of work undertaken
- whether a full written report or statement is required.

The work itself involves a varied range of duties, including:

- attending a police station to examine a prisoner, victim or police officer in relation to a wide variety of criminal offences
- occasional occupational health duties for the police force itself
- attending a scene of unexpected death to advise the police
- attending a court as a witness.

Future prospects

Radical changes in the way in which Government departments contract for part-time medical services are in the offing, and these are creating a climate of uncertainty among GPs (and other doctors) who have traditionally undertaken this work. The life assurance industry is also reviewing its methods of assessing risks and questioning the value of the medical examination and report.

There are no signs of any general expansion in the demand for private general practice. Like other activities, this is affected by the economic climate and its prevalence is strongly influenced by specific local socio-economic and cultural factors. It is heavily concentrated in particular localities where there is a predominance of foreign residents and patients with high disposable incomes.

The prospects for non-NHS part-time work for GPs are not favourable. The current economic climate has taken its toll on the opportunities for work in occupational medicine by bringing in its wake contractions and closures among many small businesses. Other firms have merged and rationalized their arrangements for occupational health medicine. However, more extensive and stringent health and safety laws may generate some expansion in this work.

12 Practice Accounts

This chapter concentrates on the basic principles of accounting as they apply to partnerships, because a very large majority of GPs work in them and also because almost all new GP principals enter general practice by joining an existing partnership. However, the basic accounting principles and methodology described below obviously apply equally to single-handed practitioners.

Partnership accounts provide a crucial record of a practice's profit for the accounting year and also show its financial worth on the balance sheet date. They also provide the Inland Revenue with information on which to assess the tax due from the partnership. Most importantly, the accounts should enable partners to review their practice's performance and plan its future development. They must therefore summarize clearly and concisely the practice's income and expenses and its net worth, and provide enough information to analyse its performance, including making comparisons with GPs' intended average gross and average net remuneration.

The income and expenditure account

This summarizes income – including investment income – and expenditure for the year. It is helpful to include the previous year's figures as comparatives so that partners can readily compare these with this year's performance. The following principles should be followed when preparing partnership accounts.

The grossing-up principle

As the Review Body pay award takes account of the level of expenses shown in GPs' accounts, together with personal claims for expenses and business interest relief included in their tax returns, it is important that all expenses are shown gross in the accounts. The NHS General Medical Services Statement of Fees and Allowances, (the Red Book) advises that all income and expenses should be shown gross in the accounts, and that, for example, staff costs should not be netted off against staff reimbursements, or premises costs against rent and rates reimbursements.

The accruals basis

The income and expenditure account should be prepared on an accruals basis, ie in a way which reflects actual income earned and expenditure incurred during the accounting period, rather than simply cash paid out and received. This is particularly relevant to any partnership where there has been a change of partners or profit shares; in these circumstances it is essential that all income earned and expenditure incurred by the partners in the year is allocated between them in that year's accounts. The term 'debtors' refers to the amount of money due to the practice at the balance sheet date; this consists mainly of FHSA and Health Board payments due to the practice at the end of the accounting year. For example, if the accounting year ends on 30th June, the June quarter payment should be included under the heading 'debtors' and also any fees and allowances received in the September quarter payment, which nevertheless relate to money earned during the June quarter.

Valuing drugs

A stock-take needs to be made at the end of the accounting year of all drugs held by the practice. These should be valued at either cost or net realizable value, whichever is lower. Their value should be included in the

DR CROSBY & PARTNERS
INCOME AND EXPENDITURE ACCOUNT
YEAR ENDED 30 JUNE 1993

	Notes	1993		1992	
		£	£	£	£
Income					
National Health Service fees	2	211 961		176 925	
Reimbursements	3	148 511		108 985	
Appointments	4	10 151		12 866	
Other income	5	10 113		7471	
Fundholding management allowance	6	24 916		12 646	
Total income			405 652		318 893
Expenditure					
Practice expenses	7	21 269		17 760	
Premises expenses	7	8359		6857	
Staff expenses	7	132 956		102 977	
Administration expenses	7	14 622		11 206	
Finance expenses	7	17 519		20 355	
Depreciation		2311		1178	
Fundholding expenses	6	24 916		11 168	
Total expenditure			221 952		171 501
			183 700		147 392
Investment income					
Bank interest receivable		766		211	
Building society interest receivable		1722		2101	
			2488		2312
Net profit for the year			186 188		149 704

Allocation of profits

	Prior shares £	Share of balance £	1993 Total £	1992 Total £
Dr Crosby	11 063	38 241	49 304	41 603
Dr Stills	10 814	38 240	49 054	41 056
Dr Nash	6523	38 240	44 763	35 428
Dr Young	6791	36 276	43 067	31 617
	35 191	150 997	186 188	149 704

Figure 12.1   A sample income and expenditure account, showing allocation of profits

balance sheet as an asset, being a part of the practice's net worth. Thus, if a partner retires from the practice, he or she has a share in the practice's stock of drugs, as valued at the end of the accounting year.

Depreciation

This charge is included in the income and expenditure account to enable the original cost of an asset to be spread over its useful life. The appropriate proportion of the original cost of an asset should be included in the expenses for each year, rather than reducing the profit of the year of actual purchase by the whole amount of its original cost. The partners (on the advice of their accountants) should decide which depreciation rates to apply to their assets. Once these have been decided they should be applied consistently. The following depreciation rates are commonly used:

- computer equipment   33⅓% per annum
- medical equipment   20% per annum
- furniture and fittings   10% per annum
- office equipment   20% per annum
- surgery premises   not normally depreciated.

Since practices can choose their own depreciation rates, the Inland Revenue does not give tax relief on the amount of depreciation included in the accounts. Instead, it allows tax relief on the purchase of fixed assets by means of standardized capital allowances.

Allocating profits to partners

When the profit for the accounting period has been calculated, it is then distributed among the partners according to the practice's profit sharing arrangements. If there are no changes in either the partnership or its profit sharing ratios during the year, this should be a comparatively straight-forward exercise. However, if such changes have occurred, it is necessary to allocate the profit by reference to the various profit sharing periods. This may be done by attempting to allocate it accurately between different profit sharing periods, such that income earned and expenditure incurred in these periods is identified and attributed to the relevant periods. Alternatively, these may be apportioned on a time basis, which means that if a new partner is admitted half-way through a year, half of the profits would be allocated to the first period and half to the second.

Obviously if the appointment or retirement of a partner is likely to affect significantly the practice's profitability, it may be advisable to apportion the income on a best estimate of the actual basis. However, because it is often extremely difficult to allocate expenses on a strictly actual basis, it may be fairer (and certainly much simpler) to apportion expenses on a time basis.

In principle, all items of practice income and expenditure must be included in the accounts so that the profit accurately reflects what is actually being generated by the practice. However, some practices have agreed that not all income should be shared among the partners according to their profit sharing ratios. Instead, income from sources such as the seniority allowance, night visit fees and the postgraduate education allowance may be retained on a personal basis by individual partners. According to this arrangement, such income should be regarded as prior shares of income and therefore allocated to partners before the resulting balance is divided between them according to the agreed profit sharing ratios. Similarly, if not all partners own the premises, or partners own the premises in different ratios to those applying to profit shares, income and expenditure relating to ownership of the surgery should be allocated as a prior charge among property owning partners according to the ratios in which they own the premises. The net surgery income comprises FHSA and Health Board rent reimbursements less interest on partnership loans relating to the premises, and any other expenditure which it is agreed should be borne by the property owning partners.

Capital grants

If FHSA or Health Board improvement grants and fundholding management allowances are paid to a practice as a contribution towards its capital expenditure, these should be offset in the accounts against the cost of relevant assets so that only the net cost is depreciated and included in the balance sheet.

FHSA and Health Board improvement grant payments and fundholding management allowances need to be shown separately; although capital allowances may be claimed if a management allowance is paid, these cannot be claimed if an improvement grant is paid towards the cost of an asset.

Presenting the accounts

Figure 12.1 shows an example of how to lay out income and expenditure accounts for a GP practice and how to allocate profits among partners.

The notes to the accounts refer partners to more detailed information so that they can analyse the practice's performance. The various NHS fees and allowances received by the practice are shown in Figure 12.2.

The practice's income consists of four main elements: practice allowances, capitation payments, sessional payments and item of service fees. On average, a GP's income is distributed among these as follows:

- allowances   20%
- capitation payments   61%
- sessional payments   5%
- item of service payments   14%
  Total   **100%**

Practices should review how their income is distributed. A significant variation from the above pattern may point to areas where a practice can increase activity and income.

GPs are self-employed individuals for tax purposes and enter into a contract for services with their FHSAs or Health Boards. The Review Body's pay award sets the levels of various NHS fees and allowances for the year. It also determines the intended average gross remuneration and the element of that gross income which is deemed to cover indirect expenses, thereby arriving at a figure for intended average net remuneration. The intended gross and net income per principal as set by the Review Body are published in the medical press, and practices should compare their accounts with these intended average levels.

Direct reimbursement

In addition to receiving indirect reimbursements for general expenses through the generality of fees and allowances, GPs are also directly re-imbursed for practice staff, surgery premises, computers, drugs, trainee salaries, staff training and certain locum fees. It is important that these direct reimbursements are shown clearly in the accounts so that a practice can identify easily the real cost of various activities; for example, the real cost of taking on an additional member of staff is the total cost less any direct reimbursement. In general, it is essential that direct reimbursements are not netted out against expenditure, because this reduces the total amount of expenses reported to the Review Body to enable it to determine GPs' pay.

Accounting records

The information in the income and expenditure account is obtained by the practice's accountants from the practice's own accounting records. These should comprise both a cash book and a record book which includes an analysis of FHSA or Health Board income. The latter should summarize all fees and allowances received from the FHSA or Health Board during the year, dividing them into the elements shown in Figure 12.2. This provides a vital record for the practice to monitor NHS income and quickly identify any fall below the expected level.

The balance sheet

This is a statement of the practice's financial position at the end of the accounting year. It is important to note that it is merely a snap-shot of the amounts owed to and by the practice at a particular point in time. On the very next day cash may be received from a debtor, thereby increasing the amount shown as cash and reducing that shown as debtors, and in turn this cash may be used to pay a creditor. Such cash movements would not affect the practice's overall total net assets although these will change during the following year as profit is earned and drawn by partners.

The balance sheet has two distinct purposes: firstly, to ascertain whether the assets of the practice are sufficient to cover its liabilities and secondly to calculate the value of the partners' investment in the practice.

It is important to recognize that the accounts being prepared are those of the business in its own right and not those of its owners, who are the partners. This is an important distinction; these have to be seen as separate entities if their relationship (which is clearly shown in the balance sheet) is to be properly understood. Partners invest their funds in the practice as a business and therefore the balance sheet shows in the capital and current accounts the amount of the funds due to the partners. Thus the balance sheet contains:

- assets
- liabilities
- partners' funds.

Accordingly, the net assets of the partnership, which comprise its assets less its liabilities, always equal the partners' funds; thus the two halves of the balance sheet should literally balance. Figure 12.3 shows how the balance sheet distinguishes between partners' funds and the use of these

DR CROSBY & PARTNERS
NOTES TO THE ACCOUNTS
YEAR ENDED 30 JUNE 1993

2. National health service fees

	1993 £	1992 £
Allowances		
Practice allowances	22 835	21 732
Seniority	4900	3523
Postgraduate education allowance	8100	7727
Rural practice payments	428	308
Trainee supervision grant	4237	4021
	40 500	37 311
Capitation payments		
Capitation fees	94 237	83 673
Deprivation payments	5421	3987
Registration fees	3974	1864
Child health surveillance	5394	1142
Homeless and rootless payments	1200	924
Target payments:		
Cervical cytology	7789	6242
Childhood immunizations	6279	6566
Pre-school boosters	2330	1643
	126 624	106 041
Sessional payments		
Health promotion clinics	16 560	10 928
Minor surgery	1000	–
Teaching medical students	854	265
	18 414	11 193
Item of service fees		
Night visits	6531	5468
Temporary residents	1453	1215
Contraceptive services	5197	4217
Emergency treatment and INT	115	22
Maternity	8926	7092
Vaccinations and immunizations	4201	4366
	26 423	22 380
Total	211 961	176 925

Figure 12.2   Fees and allowances received by a practice

for different purposes. The various subheadings within 'employment of funds' are described below.

The difference between fixed and current assets

An asset may be defined as something owned by the business and available for its future use.

Fixed assets are those used by the business over a period of several years to earn profits, but not actually available for resale. These are depreciated to spread their cost over their working life and to apportion the cost (as far as possible) appropriately among the relevant partners.

Conversely, current assets are acquired for sale and conversion into cash during the normal course of the practice's business; for example, dispensing drugs are acquired for resale to generate profit.

The term 'debtors' is used to describe monies owed to the practice for goods or services already provided which are convertible into cash, which is itself a current asset.

The difference between current and long term liabilities

Current liabilities are amounts owed by the practice and payable within 12 months of the end of the accounting year. These include trade creditors, amounts due to former partners, capital repayments of a long-term loan due within the next 12 months, and bank overdrafts, which are always repayable on demand!

Long-term liabilities are capital amounts outstanding on loans which are repayable over a period longer than 12 months.

The total obtained by subtracting liabilities from assets is the partnership's net assets; this figure represents the net worth of the business and is equal to the partners' funds, being their investment in the practice.

Partners' funds

It helps to understand the nature of their investment in the practice if the partners' funds are divided between long-term investments (which can

DR CROSBY & PARTNERS
BALANCE SHEET
YEAR ENDED 30 JUNE 1993

	Notes	1993		1992	
		£	£	£	£
Partners' funds and tax provision					
Property capital accounts	8		106 550		100 813
Capital accounts	9		20 000		20 000
Current accounts	10		4090		6211
Taxation provisions	11		15 819		14 608
			146 459		141 632
Employment of funds					
Fixed assets	13		359 363		325 260
Current assets					
Stock of drugs		621		712	
Debtors		32 180		26 956	
Balance at building society		12 271		3479	
Cash at bank and in hand		511		8769	
		45 583		39 916	
Current liabilities					
Bank overdraft		1211		–	
Creditors		13 210		9972	
Due to former partners		597		2638	
GPFC loan		6000		–	
		21 018		12 610	
Net current assets			24 565		27 306
			383 928		352 566
Long-term liabilities					
Mortgage loans			237 469		210 934
Net assets			146 459		141 632

Figure 12.3   Division of partners' funds

only be withdrawn when they retire from the practice), and those amounts which reflect the difference between partners' profit shares for the year and their drawings from the practice. The latter represents the money which may be withdrawn from the practice when the accounts are finally agreed.

Thus the partners' funds should be divided into these categories:

- property capital accounts
- capital accounts
- current accounts
- taxation provisions.

The property capital account

This is the partners' equity in the premises and is the difference between the premises' cost or valuation and any outstanding partnership loans.

If the premises are funded by individual partners' personal loans rather than by a partnership loan, the property capital accounts should show the value of the premises and the partners' borrowing will be shown 'off' balance sheet. Personal loans may be preferred to a partnership loan because tax relief on the interest is paid on a current year basis through partners' individual tax returns, rather than on a preceding year basis if included in the practice accounts.

Capital accounts

The partners' capital account refers to the funds provided for working capital to enable the practice to run smoothly. The amount of this working capital varies between practices, reflecting the net book value of fixed assets (excluding premises) funded by the partners rather than by partnership loans, and also the value of debtors and creditors to a practice. The capital account therefore funds the purchase of fixed assets and the practice's day-to-day expenditure so that it can run without the risk of incurring an overdraft at times when income may be lower than expenditure.

The capital accounts should be established in the partners' profit sharing ratios to ensure that capital funding is on an equitable basis. A partner's share of this capital will remain in the practice until he or she leaves the practice.

Current accounts

These reflect the difference between partners' share of the profits for the year less the amount they have drawn, superannuation payments and any sum earmarked for tax. Figure 12.4 shows the information which should be included to allow each partner to analyse changes in the current account during the year.

Leave advances are included in the current account if these are withdrawn by the partners. They are effectively interest free loans repayable by deduction from the FHSA's or Health Board's quarterly payments, and they therefore do not affect a practice's profit. However, if leave advances are retained by the partnership as working capital, they should not be shown in the partners' current accounts. Any amount retained at the end of the year should be included under the heading 'creditors' in the balance sheet.

Providing for tax liabilities

The concept of sharing in joint and several liability can cause problems. At least with the tax liability, the risk of having to pay a partners's share of tax can be avoided by retaining within the practice the partnership tax which is due to be paid.

Making provision for tax payments is essentially a book-keeping exercise. Within the practice's accounts certain amounts are charged to each partner's account and credited to a tax provision account in the same partner's name. Payments to the Inland Revenue are drawn from these tax provision accounts. This does not necessarily require the tax to be deposited in a separate bank or building society account; it simply retains the cash in the partnership by preventing partners from withdrawing it from their current accounts. This retained money can be used by the practice as working capital, particularly since it is comparatively easy to plan in advance for its payment to the Inland Revenue.

This arrangement has the advantage of ensuring that when a partner leaves a practice, there is no need to ask him or her to contribute to the partnership's tax liability. It is advisable to ensure the amount set aside is sufficient to meet the preceding year tax liability up to the date of the balance sheet; thus a retiring partner should leave sufficient funds in the partnership to cover his or her share of its tax liability. So long as partners' drawings are calculated on a 'net of tax' basis, there should always be enough funds in the tax provision accounts to meet a partner's share of the tax liability regardless of when a partner retires or indeed dies in service.

10. Partners' current accounts

	Dr Crosby £	Dr Stills £	Dr Nash £	Dr Young £	Total £
Balance at 1 July 1992	1011	2196	1976	1028	6211
Profit for the year	49 304	49 054	44 763	43 067	186 188
Leave advances	1277	1277	1277	1277	5108
Cash introduced	210	–	–	–	210
Income tax repaid	971	1134	56	–	2161
	52 773	53 661	48 072	45 372	199 878
Monthly drawings	29 914	26 699	27 886	28 719	113 218
Fees retained privately	681	315	100	750	1846
Payment of personal expenses	210	–	–	195	405
Wives' salaries	2521	2422	2456	–	7399
Leave payments withdrawn	1277	1277	1277	1277	5108
Prior shares withdrawn	6525	6662	2025	2025	17 237
Transfers to property capital accounts (note 8)	1434	1435	1434	1434	5737
Transfers to tax provisions (note 11)	5829	6639	7121	5111	24 700
PAYE on appointments	–	1211	519	519	2249
Class 1 NIC	–	283	127	127	537
Class 2 NIC	252	252	252	252	1008
Superannuation:					
Standard	2569	2411	2201	2032	9213
Added years – variable	–	1211	576	–	1787
Appointments	–	572	–	572	1144
Leave advances repaid	1050	1050	1050	1050	4200
	52 262	52 439	47 024	44 063	195 788
Balance at 30 June 1993	511	1222	1048	1309	4090

Figure 12.4 Partners' current accounts

To illustrate this, the amount of tax provision in accounts for the year ended 30 June 1993 should be sufficient to cover the whole of the 1992/93 liability and any earlier years not yet finally settled, and also one-quarter of the 1993/94 tax liability for the period from 6 April to 30 June 1993.

Since the tax liability for the whole of the current year and the next fiscal year (being based on the current year's accounts) is known, it is helpful for partners to be given information concerning it so that they can plan their own personal cash flow.

Figure 12.5 illustrates a partnership taxation provision, and movements within the individual partners' tax provision accounts are shown in Figure 12.6.

Fundholding and partnership accounts

Fundholders have to produce a separate account for their fundholding activities and these must be drawn up to 31 March each year, regardless of the accounting year of the main practice account. However, there is some interaction between the fundholding and main practice accounts.

The management allowance

This is paid to a practice to cover fundholding management expenses. Thus, in both the preparatory year and the fundholding years, the allowance and its related expenditure must be shown as separate items in the income and expenditure account if it is used to pay for revenue expense items. This ensures that the expenditure is included gross for Review Body purposes.

Reimbursement of capital expenditure, both out of the management allowance and from the savings account, should be shown in the same way as grants in the fixed asset note to the accounts, thus reducing the cost of the assets to the amount contributed by the practice. In most cases this will be nil. However, capital allowances may be claimed on any net amount contributed to the cost of the asset by the practice.

The fundholding bank account

Funds held in this account are not owned by a practice's partners. Therefore the account should be clearly annotated by the bank as a fundholding account, and should not be referred to in the practice balance sheet. Any interest charged on this account should be paid from the

11. Partnership taxation provision

Assuming the practice continues to pay income tax on a preceding year basis and at current rates of tax, provision has been made in the accounts for the year for income tax and Class 4 NIC liabilities up to 30 June 1993.

		£
1991/92	estimated repayment due	(1393)
1992/93	balance of liability	14 854
1993/94	on preceding year basis for the period 6 April	
	1993 – 30 June 1993	2358
		15 819

The 1993/94 income tax and Class 4 NIC liabilities (against which £2358 has been provided) are estimated to be:

		£
1993/94	due 1 January 1994	4750
	due 1 July 1994	4750
		9500

No provision has been made in these accounts for 1994/95 income tax and Class 4 NIC liabilities (which are based on results to 30 June 1993) which are estimated to be:

		£
1994/95	due 1 January 1995	7500
	due 1 July 1995	7500
		15 000

Figure 12.5   A partnership tax provision

12. Movements on taxation provision

	Dr Crosby £	Dr Stills £	Dr Nash £	Dr Young £	Subtotal £	Payments on account £	Total £
Provision brought forward at 1 July 1992	12 124	10 457	13 194	11 122	46 897	(32 289)	14 608
Charge/(release) for:							
1991/92	(1173)	40	(1020)	(5)	(2158)		(2158)
1992/93	6381	6088	7832	4199	24 500		24 500
1993/94	621	511	309	917	2358		2358
Total charge for year	5829	6639	7121	5111	24 700		24 700
(Paid)/repaid during year for:							
1991/92						(11 449)	(11 449)
1992/93						(12 040)	(12 040)
Total payment						(23 489)	(23 489)
Allocation of payment for:							
1990/91	(5013)	(6616)	(6884)	(4738)	(23 251)	23 251	–
Provision carried forward	12 940	10 480	13 431	11 495	48 346	(32 527)	15 819
Representing:							
1991/92	5598	4047	6055	3394	19 094	(20 487)	(1393)
1992/93	6721	5922	7067	7184	26 894	(12 040)	14 854
1993/94	621	511	309	917	2358	–	2358
	12 940	10 480	13 431	11 495	48 346	(32 527)	15 819

Figure 12.6   Movements on partners' tax provision accounts

management allowance. The partners are not entitled to any interest receiving on the fundholding account; it must be paid to the FHSA or Health Board. Therefore, such interest should not be shown as income in the partnership accounts or in partners' personal tax returns.

Practice staff reimbursement

Reimbursement out of the fundholding staff fund to the partnership must be included in the practice accounts as practice staff refunds, and care should be taken to ensure that all monies due at the year end are included. If too much or too little cash has been transferred from the fundholding bank account, a balance will appear on the fundholding balance sheet as either a debtor or creditor under the heading of general practice account, and an equal and opposite entry should appear in the partnership balance sheet.

Figure 12.7 shows the note which should appear in the partnership accounts summarizing the expenditure from the fundholding management allowance and the allowance received. It will be seen that the allowance received in respect of revenue items totalled £24,916, and the relevant expenditure is shown in the income and expenditure account in Figure 12.1. The allowance received to reimburse capital acquisitions totalled £8084, and will be set off against the cost of those items in the fixed assets note, thereby reducing the value of these fixed assets in the balance sheet.

Partners' personal expenses

Partners' personal expenses, such as the cost of running cars, can be shown in either the partnership accounts or claimed against tax through their personal tax returns.

The Inland Revenue treats the assessable profits for GPs as being the profit as shown in the accounts less the total of the partners' personal expense claims for the same period. Therefore the way in which these expenses are treated does not affect either the timing or the level of tax relief allowed.

Similarly, the Review Body includes partners' personal expense claims in their calculation of total expenses, and again there is no difference between claiming the expenses through the practice accounts or a personal tax return. It is important to note that under the new tax system, expenses and capital allowances will only be able to be claimed on the partnership return. It will therefore be necessary for partners to disclose their personal

6. Fundholding management allowance

		1993 £		1992 £
Allowance received for capital assets		8084		2350
Allowance received for revenue expenditure		24 916		12 646
		33 000		14 996
Capital expenditure				
Computer equipment	6619		–	
Medical equipment	1215		1454	
Furniture and fittings	250		896	
		8084		2350
Revenue expenditure				
Staff	17 456		5432	
Locum payments	2200		2000	
Training	2468		1851	
Computer costs and maintenance	1246		563	
Accountancy	1546		1176	
Other	–		146	
		24 916		11 168
Net income		–		1478

Figure 12.7 Summary of expenditure from the fundholding management allowance

expenses and capital allowances to their partners so that they can be incorporated in the personal expenses claim.

The treatment chosen should be that which is most equitable between the partners. If expenses are incurred by all partners at a similar level, they may be included in the partnership accounts without the risk of one partner bearing another's expenses.

However, if there is any element of personal choice which could affect expense levels, it is much fairer to regard personal expenditure as being paid out of that partner's profit share and tax relief should be claimed on personal expense claims. Cars are probably the best example of this kind of expenditure; partners usually prefer to buy cars costing significantly different amounts and have widely differing levels of private usage.

The proportion of allowable motoring costs is based on the business usage proportion; thus if a partner is able to claim 80% of usage as business usage, this proportion of motoring costs will be eligible for tax relief. Capital allowances are available on the car irrespective of whether it is owned by the partnership or the partner, and the same rules apply.

Examples of business expenses frequently claimed as personal expenses include:

- surgery facilities in private homes
- home study facilities
- medical books and journals
- courses and conferences
- home telephone bills
- laundry and cleaning
- spouse's salary for telephone answering, secretarial and counselling services.

13 Taxation

This chapter explains how GPs' remuneration is taxed under the rules which apply to all self-employed persons, whether or not they work in partnerships. However, because most GPs work as partners, it concentrates on partnership taxation.

Taxation can often be complex, but for the self-employed and partnerships it is particularly complicated. This is why all GPs should obtain advice and assistance from a qualified and experienced accountant who has a detailed knowledge of their remuneration arrangements. Once an accountant has been engaged, the practice should not negotiate or correspond directly with the tax office; all contact should be through the professional accountant. Nevertheless, even if GPs rely on accountants to look after their tax affairs, they themselves should also understand the basic principles and rules governing taxation.

Inspection and collection

From the standpoint of the taxpayer the Inland Revenue is divided into two functions: assessment (i.e. 'inspection') and collection. The inspector of taxes assesses a taxpayer's liability and issues a notice of assessment, whereas the collector of taxes issues the demand for payment, collects the tax and takes enforcement proceedings if it is not paid.

Employment and self-employment: schedules D and E

For the majority of GPs, their income tax will be governed mostly by schedule D, although schedule E may apply to income from any salaried appointments they may hold. However, all GPs will have been assessed for tax under schedule E at some stage in their careers when they were working as employees, and have had deductions made from their salaries under PAYE. On the other hand, as self-employed contractors GPs are assessed under schedule D. Because the method of assessment is different under each schedule, it is important to understand how this works.

The main differences lie in the treatment of expenses, the basis of assessment, and the date of payment of tax. In many circumstances, schedules D and E overlap and some GPs receive income under both headings concurrently. If this occurs in a partnership quite complicated taxation problems can arise. Sometimes it is not immediately clear whether income from an appointment should be assessed under schedule D or E; for example, payments made for clinical assistant appointments in GP and community hospitals where the practice as a whole provides the required services.

Year of assessment

Taxation is organized according to tax years, termed 'years of assessment' or 'fiscal years'. The tax year runs from 6 April in one calendar year to 5 April in the next; the year from 6 April 1994 to 5 April 1995 is designated the 1994/95 tax year.

The basis of assessment

Currently a major advantage of schedule D is that it allows tax to be paid in arrears, over a period of up to two years after the income was earned. (The Government is committed to changing arrangements for taxing the self-employed and these changes are explained below.) This arrangement arises from a preceding year basis of assessment, whereby profits charged to tax in any year of assessment are based upon the profits earned in the accounting period ending within the preceding tax year. Because the tax year runs from 6 April in one year to 5 April in the next, if a practice has its accounts made up to 30 June 1994 its profits will be assessed in the tax year 1995/96. But if these profits were made up for the year to 31 March 1994, they would be assessed for tax a year earlier, in the 1994/95 year.

Partnership taxation

Calculating taxable profits

The annual accounts of a practice show the net profits earned during the year and these are calculated by deducting total expenditure from total income. However, an adjustment usually has to be made to the net profits to obtain the practice's taxable profits. This is because the accounts may include expenditure which the Inland Revenue does not regard as an allowable expense; for example, the cost of entertainment, capital expense such as legal fees relating to a new surgery, the element of personal use of any type of expenditure, interest charged by the Inland Revenue on late payment of tax, and depreciation. Depreciation is disallowed because a practice may choose to depreciate its fixed assets at any rate ranging from, say, 100% in the first year to 10% per annum.

Capital allowances

Although the Inland Revenue disallows any depreciation charged in the accounts, it allows tax relief through a system of capital allowances which provides a standardized rate of depreciation of 25% per annum on a reducing balance basis. If the expenditure includes an element of private use, the capital allowance is limited to that proportion which can be attributed to strictly business use. In the case of cars, the cost on which the capital allowance is calculated is restricted to £12,000 for cars purchased after 10 March 1992 and £8000 for those purchased prior to that date. When a car is sold, a balancing allowance is allowed if the tax relief so far

A GP purchases a car for £13 000 on 1 April 1992 and claims 80% business usage.

		£	Writing down allowance £
Year 1	Cost	13 000	
	WDA – restricted 25% × 12 000	(3000) × 80%	2400
		10 000	
Year 2	WDA at 25%	(2500) × 80%	2000
		7500	
Year 3	WDA at 25%	(1875) × 80%	1500
		5625	
Year 4	Sale proceeds	(5000)	
		625	
Balancing allowance		625 × 80%	500
		Nil	

Figure 13.1   Capital allowances on cars

allowed does not cover the net cost of the car (the difference between original purchase price and second hand sale price). A balancing charge may be made if too much tax relief has already been allowed (*see* Figure 13.1).

It should be noted that there was a special 40% first year allowance on new assets (excluding cars) bought between 1 November 1992 and 31 October 1993. This replaced the 25% writing down allowance normally claimed in the year of purchase.

The final adjustment that needs to be made to the profits shown in the accounts to calculate profit assessable for tax, is to deduct any income which is either non-taxable (eg a repayment of overpaid tax) or assessed on the individual partners' tax returns under a separate assessment (eg bank or building society interest, or rental income). However, the rent reimbursement, or cost/notional rent received from the FHSA or Health Board should not be deducted as rental income because this is part of the practice profits taxable under Schedule D. Further adjustment should be made to allow for any income received from other appointments, which has already been taxed at source under PAYE.

Personal expense claims

The Inland Revenue considers the taxable profit of a practice to be the tax adjusted profit as shown in its accounts, less the partnership capital allowances, partners' personal expense claims, and any other capital allowances applying to that period.

Therefore it does not affect either the amount or the timing of the tax relief, whether expenses are included in the practice accounts or claimed individually via partners' personal expense claims. It is preferable to claim any expense which varies between partners through their personal expense returns rather than through the practice accounts. This ensures that partners are not subsidizing each others' expenses, particularly those relating to cars where the purchase price and running costs can vary greatly between partners. It also applies to those expenses which are not necessarily incurred by all partners, eg spouses' salaries for secretarial and telephone answering services.

Allocating the assessable profit – Preceding year basis

Having calculated the assessable profits, the next step is to allocate them between the partners according to the profit sharing ratios prevailing during the tax year in which the profit is assessed, and not according to the ratios applicable to the period when the profits were actually earned. This crucial distinction between earning profits and paying tax on them can be particularly confusing. To ensure partners obtain tax relief on their own personal expenses and personal capital allowances, it is preferable to treat these as a prior expense of the individuals, in the same way as any income (such as seniority allowances) which is retained by individual partners is treated as a prior share of the profits.

These amounts can then be allocated to the individual partners before the balance of the assessable profit is allocated between them according to the profit sharing ratios appertaining to the tax year.

Calculating the tax liability

When the assessment has been allocated between partners it is necessary to look at each partner's individual tax position to calculate the tax payable. The following should be deducted from each individual partner's share in respect of the actual tax year:

- any personal allowances and reliefs

- personal pension premiums and superannuation
- interest on loans qualifying for tax relief.

The income tax rates for each partner are then applied to his or her share of the net taxable profit to calculate income tax and Class 4 NIC liabilities.

Joint and several liability

Having calculated each individual's income tax and Class 4 NIC liabilities, these are added together to obtain the total partnership tax liability. The Inland Revenue then issues a single assessment on the whole partnership for the total tax and Class 4 NIC due because the partners carry joint and several liability for the partnership tax.

The Inland Revenue requires the partnership to pay the tax, not the individual partners. This is why it is advisable for every partnership to plan for the amount of tax due to be retained by the partnership so that there is no risk of a partner being unable to meet his or her share of the joint liability.

This concept of joint and several liability for tax will cease on the introduction of the new current year basis of tax.

Preceding year basis of assessment

Under the present tax system, profits of partnerships and sole practitioners are taxed on what is known as a preceding year basis; ie the assessment for a tax year is based on the profits of the accounting period ending in the previous tax year. For example, if the annual accounts are for a period ending on 31 March 1993, which is in the tax year 1992/93, the profits will be assessed in the 1993/94 tax year (*see* Figure 13.2). However, if the accounts are for the year ending 30 April 1993, because this ends in the tax year 1993/94 the profits will be assessed in 1994/95 (*see* Figure 13.3).

If profits are continuing to rise, it is preferable to choose an accounting year ending early in the new tax year in order to extend the period between earning profits and paying tax on them. This is why 30 April is the ideal year end date for most self-employed people. However, for GPs it is convenient to have a date coterminous with an FHSA quarter day; 30 June is therefore the optimum date, being the first quarter day after 6 April, when the tax year begins.

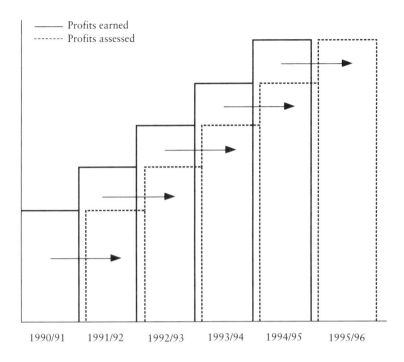

Figure 13.2 Profits assessable under the preceding year basis of assessment, accounting year end 31 March

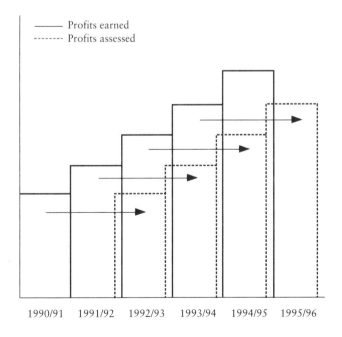

Figure 13.3 Profits assessable under the preceding year basis of assessment, accounting year end 30 April

A case has been made for GPs to use 31 March as the end date of their accounting year because the Doctors' and Dentists' Review Body bases its expenses evidence on anonymized samples of GPs' tax returns drawn from practices whose accounting year end on 31 March. However, the BMA's General Medical Services Committee recognizes that many GPs are now using the most tax advantageous year end date and it is therefore considering how the sample survey might be changed to include practices with other accounting year end dates.

The cash flow advantage of the optimum choice of accounting year end can be seen in Figures 13.2 and 13.3. Furthermore, a retiring partner can benefit from receiving an additional slice of tax free income: the difference between actual profits earned and profits assessed in the last two years of partnership, if a continuation election has been made.

Taxing a new partnership

Tax assessment on a normal preceding year basis lags between one and two years behind the period when profits are earned. This arrangement cannot apply at the start of a new practice, special 'opening' year rules apply:

- the first year is assessed on actual profits earned from the start of the partnership to the following 5 April
- the second year is assessed on the profits earned in the first 12 months
- the third year is assessed on profits earned in the accounting year ending in the immediately preceding tax year (i.e. the normal preceding year basis begins to apply).

For example, if a practice commences on 1 July 1993 the opening year assessments will be:

1993/94   actual profits earned from 1 July 1993 to 5 April 1994

1994/95   profits earned from 1 July 1993 to 30 June 1994

1995/96   profits earned in the year ended 30 June 1994.

Accordingly, the opening year forms the basis of between two and three years' assessments to establish the practice on the preceding year basis. However, if the profits actually earned in the second and third years of assessment are lower than the profits that would have been taxed according to these rules, the practice can elect to be taxed on the actual profits earned in those two years.

Taxing a partnership at its cessation – preceding year basis

When the partnership ends there will be profits covering a period of between one and two years which do not form the basis of any assessment.

The assessment for the period from 6 April to the date of cessation is based upon actual profits earned during that period. The assessments for the two immediately previous years may, at the discretion of the Inland Revenue, be increased to the actual profits of those two years.

For example, if a practice ceased on 30 June 1993, the assessment would be:

1990/91	year ended 30 June 1989
1991/92	year ended 30 June 1990 or increased to profits earned from 6 April 1991 to 5 April 1992
1992/93	year ended 30 June 1991 or increased to profits earned from 6 April 1992 to 5 April 1993

Therefore either profits from 1 July 1991 to 5 April 1993 or profits from 1 July 1989 to 5 April 1991 will be untaxed.

Partnership changes

If there is a change in the partnership because a partner retires or a new partner is appointed, the partnership automatically ends for tax purposes unless all partners affected join in an 'election' to treat the partnership as a continuing firm. If this is done, tax assessments continue to be made on the normal preceding year basis. In the case of a deceased partner, the election has to be signed by a personal representative. This continuation election must be submitted to the Inland Revenue within two years of the partnership change.

If a continuation election is not made, then the old partnership is treated as having ceased for tax purposes so that cessation rules then apply. Special rules known as the 'deemed commencement rules' apply. These require the new partnership to be assessed on the basis of actual profits for each of its first four years of assessment. Only in the fifth year of assessment can the partnership return to a normal preceding year basis of assessment.

Since the consequent loss of a preceding year basis of assessment for a total of some six years (taking the old and new partnerships together) can be very costly, it is advisable to include a clause in the partnership agreement binding all partners to signing a continuation election when recommended to do so by the partnership accountant.

If for any reason a particular partner loses out by signing a continuation election (even though it benefits the partnership as a whole) it may be advisable to make an equity adjustment between the partners so that the disadvantaged partner is compensated from the others' combined tax gains.

Proposed changes to the taxation of the self-employed

The Government plans to implement proposals for simplifying the taxation of the self-employed. The provisions set out below are based on the Finance Bill which was published on 11 January 1994 prior to any amendments which may arise before the new legislation is finally incorporated in the Finance Act 1994.

It is proposed to:

- abolish the complex preceding year basis of assessment for the self-employed
- abolish partners' joint and several liability for partnership tax
- allow taxpayers who complete a tax return to choose between assessing themselves and working out how much tax is due on their total income (in which case they would have to submit their tax return by 31 January following the end of the tax year), or allowing the Inland Revenue to make the assessment (in which case the tax return would have to be submitted by 1 October following the end of the tax year)
- abolish the 'schedular' system, thus bringing together all the taxpayer's income from all sources on one tax statement, with one tax bill.

The new rules relating to self-assessment and the abolition of the 'schedular' system are scheduled to take effect from the tax year 1996/97.

Abolishing the preceding year basis

The preceding year basis of assessment will be replaced by a current year basis, so that the accounting period ending in the tax year will form the basis of assessment for that year.

It had been suggested in an earlier consultative document that fiscal accounting should be compulsory, that is, all self-employed individuals

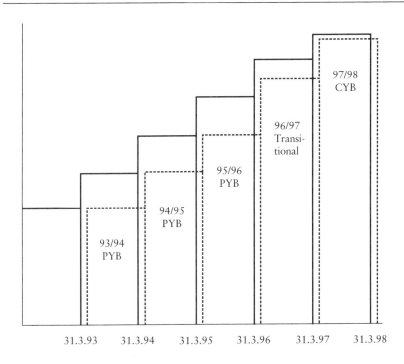

Figure 13.4   Introduction of current year basis (CYB) for accounting year end 31 March

would have to draw up their accounts to 5 April. This has been dropped and the self-employed will continue to choose their own accounting year end.

Indeed, under the current year basis of assessment, the choice of an optimum accounting date will continue to be important. For example, liability for the first full year of the new system (1997/98) would be based on the accounting period ending in the year 5 April 1998. This could be either the year ending 31 March 1998 or the year ending 30 April 1997. Therefore, it is still possible to defer the payment of tax on profits by choosing the optimum accounting date (*see* Figs. 13.4 and 13.5).

Under the current year basis, it is proposed that tax will still be payable in two equal interim instalments on 31 January in the tax year and 31 July following the end of the tax year. Each instalment will be based on one half of the actual tax liability for the previous year, with any balance of outstanding tax due for the current year payable on the following 31 January. Therefore, for the tax year 1997/98, the two interim instalments would be payable on 31 January 1998 and 31 July 1998, with any balance

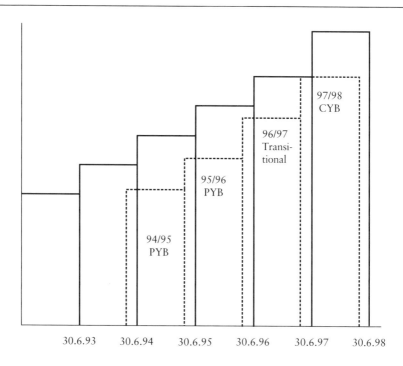

Figure 13.5   Introduction of the current year basis of assessment (CYB) for accounting year end 30 June

due payable on 31 January 1999. This still applies if your year end is 30 June 1997 or 31 March 1998.

Tax returns

Partners will have to submit personal tax returns by 31 January following the end of the tax year which will include his or her share of the partnership profit assessable in that tax year. The return will also have to include the calculation of the income tax and any capital gains tax liability. If the taxpayer prefers that the Revenue calculate the tax payable the return would have to be submitted by 30 September following the end of the tax year.

Partnerships will also have to file a separate partnership return which will have the same filing date of 31 January following the end of the tax year. For example, a partnership would have to submit its return for 1997/98 by 1 January 1999 which would incorporate the profits based on its accounting period ending in the year ended 5 April 1998, which could therefore be the year ended 31 March 1998 or the year ended 30 June 1997. The return will have to be submitted by a nominated partner and will include a list of partners, their private addresses and tax references. It will also include a partnership statement showing the trading profit or loss, together with bank interest and any other sources of income, and also capital gains and charges on income, and the allocation of these profits between the partners.

Penalties

There will be a system of penalties to encourage people to submit returns on time and to pay their tax by the due dates. There will be three types of penalties:

- surcharges for the late payment of tax
- penalties for the late submission of returns, and
- other penalties.

Surcharges for the late payment of tax

These will not apply to the two interim payments, but if the tax paid by 31 January following the year of assessment is less than the tax due, the surcharge will be:

- tax paid up to 28 days of the due date, that is, normally by 28 February   Nil

- tax paid between 28 days and 6 months of the due date   5% of that tax

- tax paid more than 6 months after the due date   10% of that tax

Interest is payable in addition to the surcharge and surcharges themselves will carry interest. The Revenue will have the right to mitigate such surcharges if they see fit.

Penalties for the late submission of returns

The penalty for the failure to submit a Return will be £100 plus up to £60 a day for any failure continuing after the Commissioners have directed a return to be submitted.

If the return is submitted more than 6 months late, the penalty is £200 instead of £100 and, if more than 12 months late, there will be a tax-related penalty of 100% of the tax. These penalties apply to both personal and partnership tax returns.

Other penalties

There will also be a penalty of up to 10% of the tax for incorrect returns. In the case of a partnership return, each partner is liable for the penalty in respect of his share of the profits.

Interest

Interest will apply to interim payments as well as final payments and run from the due date of payment.

The choice of a favourable accounting date can defer submission of the accounts and computations, and payment of the final tax liability, by between 10 and 21 months after the end of the accounting year. Given the application of interest and penalties set out above, it could be advantageous to avoid unnecessarily tight deadlines.

However, in choosing the most appropriate accounting year end, consideration must also be given to the tax position of retiring partners which is considered on pages 169–90.

The transitional year

It is proposed that 1996/97 will be a transitional year. To move smoothly from the preceding year basis system of tax to the current year basis, 1996/97 will be taxed on the profit for 12 months out of the period between the basis periods for 1995/96 and 1997/98. This will generally be one half of the profits for the two-year period ending in 1996/97.

Accordingly, with a 30 June year end, 1996/97 will be taxed on one half of the profits for the year ended 30 June 1995 and the year ended 30 June 1996. This means that, effectively, the equivalent of one year's profits will not be taxed.

Although this is an attractive idea, it must be remembered that one year's expenses will not be allowed against income tax. It is therefore important to review the timing of expenditure and where possible bring expenditure forward to before the commencement of the first accounting period which will be assessable in 1996/97; for example, with a June year end, incur expenditure before 30 June 1994 or defer it until after the end of the second relevant accounting period (eg after 30 June 1996). This would apply particularly to repairs and renewals, and redecoration where some flexibility in the timing of the expenditure may be available.

It is also worth considering buying rather than leasing assets as capital allowances will not be affected by the 24 month averaging rule. Full relief will therefore be available via the capital allowance system whereas tax relief will only be available on half the lease cost in that two year period.

If the practice makes pension contributions for its staff, contributions can be paid before the end of the year which forms the basis for 1995/96 so as to minimize any contribution paid in the period assessable in 1996/97.

In these circumstances, it may also be worthwhile ensuring that new borrowings are taken out as personal rather than partnership loans. Tax relief would then be obtained individually on an actual year basis through the individual partners' personal tax returns. This is usually advantageous in any circumstances because it accelerates the tax relief. However, following the publication of an Inland Revenue press release on 31 March 1994 containing various proposed anti-avoidance provisions, existing partnership loans can only be converted into personal loans if this is being done for bona fide commercial reasons, and not solely to obtain a tax advantage. It is therefore particularly important that loans are now initially set up in the most tax efficient way.

Partnership changes

The concept of joint and several liability to tax on a partnership assessment will no longer apply. Instead a partner's share of partnership profits will be treated as a separate trade carried out by the partner. Therefore a partner joining or leaving a practice will have no effect on the other continuing partners.

An incoming partner will be treated as if he had set up a new business when he joins the partnership and hence the opening year rules will apply to that partner. An outgoing partner will be treated as if his business had ceased and therefore the cessation rules will apply to his share of profit and overlap relief will be available to offset against that final assessable profit. These special rules are set out below.

Starting and ending partnerships

It had originally been announced that no special rules would be required for partnership commencements and cessations.

These special rules, as operated under the existing preceding year basis system, caused the main mismatch between profits earned and profits taxed, and make it difficult for most taxpayers to understand how the system works.

Under the proposals in the Finance Bill, the broad principle remains that over the lifetime of a business all profits earned will be taxed once and only once.

However, there are now some proposals for special rules to apply to the opening and closing years of a business, and also where there is a change of accounting date, resulting in there not being a 12 month period ending in the year of assessment.

Opening year rules

The following basis periods will apply to new businesses and to a new partner joining the practice.

Year 1 Actual profit from commencement to 5 April

Year 2 either,

  (a)   12 months ending with the accounting date in the year, or

  (b)   12 months from commencement date, if there is no such 12-month period

Year 3 12 months ending with the accounting date.

For example, the following basis periods would apply if a practice commenced on 1 July 1998 and alternatively made up its accounts to:

(i)   30 June 1999, or

(ii)   30 April 2000, or

(iii)   31 March 2000.

	(i)	(ii)	(iii)
Yr 1 1998/99	9 months to 5.4.99	9 months to 5.4.99	9 months to 5.4.99
Yr 2 1999/00	12 months to 30.6.99 (a)	12 months to 30.6.99 (b)	12 months to 31.3.00 (a)
Yr 3 2000/01	12 months to 30.6.00	12 months to 30.4.00	12 months to 31.3.01

Taking the example in (i) above, the profits from 1 July 1998 to 5 April 1999 will be taxed twice, once in 1998/99 and again in 1999/2000. This period is therefore treated as an overlap and overlap relief will be available on these profits as explained on page 169.

Closing year rules

When a practice ceases, the profits to be taken into account for the last year will be those arising from the end of the basis period in the preceding year.

For example, if a practice which made up its accounts to 30 June each year ceases on 30 June 2000, the assessable profits would be:

1999/2000   year to 30 June 1999

2000/2001   12 months from 1 July 1999 to 30 June 2000.

However, if instead of ceasing on 30 June 2000, it made up its final accounts to 31 March 2001, the position would then be:

1999/2000   year to 30 June 1999

2000/2001   21 months from 1 July 1999 to 31 March 2001.

Accordingly, in the first and last year of a business, a period other than 12 months can fall to be taxed.

These closing year rules will apply to individual partners when they retire from the practice.

It will be seen that under the new system a partner retiring on 30 June 2000 will pay tax on the whole of the 2000/2001 assessment even though he has retired just three months into that tax year.

This additional nine months liability will however be reduced by overlap relief which in the case of a 30 June year end will generally be 9/12ths of the 1997/98 assessable profits (see page 170).

If, instead of drawing accounts up to 30 June, a practice draws its accounts up to 31 March, then a partner would not suffer any charge to tax after the date of retirement from the practice. For example, a practice makes up its accounts to 31 March 2000 and a partner retires on that date. His final assessable profit would be: 1999/2000 year to 31 March 2000.

However, if the practice had made up its accounts to 31 March in 1997/98 then there would be no overlap relief arising from that period as the assessable profits would have been based on the year ended 31 March 1998.

Overlap relief

As referred to above, the Finance Bill has introduced a new form of relief called overlap relief which will apply where profits are taxed more than once. However, the relief will only be given on the earlier of:

- a change in the accounting date which results in an assessment based on a period of more than 12 months, or
- the cessation of the trade. This applies to a partner leaving a practice but in that case would affect only the outgoing partner.

For businesses commencing before 6 April 1994, 1996/97 is the transitional year between the two tax systems and 1997/98 is the first full year of the new system. Taking the example of a partner whose share of the profits in the year ended 30 June 1997 is £60,000, the assessment would be:

1997/98   01.07.96 to 30.06.97   £60,000

The period 1 July 1996 to 5 April 1997 is treated as an overlap period. Overlap relief of £45,000 will be available either when the whole practice ceases, or on that partner's retirement, or in a year for which the basis period is longer than 12 months (ie if there is a change of accounting date).

This relief will therefore be available to most partners as a Case II deduction when they retire in their final year of assessment. This is intended to compensate them for the fact that under the new current year system, if a partner were to retire on say 30 June 1998, then he would share in the full 1998/99 assessment rather than in just 3/12ths of that assessment as he would do under the present system. The overlap relief is accordingly offset against that final assessment in order to reduce that liability.

Capital allowances and personal expenses

The treatment for the relief of capital allowances is to change to that currently used for companies. Capital allowances will accordingly be treated as a deduction in computing trading profits in the same way as expenses are treated. The relief for capital allowances will therefore be tied to the accounting period rather than the year of assessment.

Relief for all the partners' personal capital allowances and personal expense claims will also be given in the same way and these will have to be included on the partnership tax return as a deduction from the accounts profit for relief to be claimed.

New businesses commencing after 5 April 1994

In the case of a new practice starting up after 5 April 1994, the new current year basis will apply immediately. Therefore the opening year rules set out on page 168 will apply, and also partners would be subject to individual assessment on their share of the practice profits. This position also applies to partnerships deemed to have commenced following a cessation for tax purposes after 5 April 1994.

The application of these opening year rules could present a practical problem for partners joining a practice before 5 April in a tax year where the accounts are drawn up to a date late in the calendar year. For example, a partner joining a practice on 1 February 1999 where the partnership accounts are made up to 31 December 1999 would have to include on his tax return for the year 1998/99 his share of the profits for the period from 1 February to 5 April 1999. This return must be submitted by 31 January 2000, although it is very unlikely the partnership accounts for the year ended 31 December 1999 could be finalized by then.

On any partnership changes occurring between 6 April 1994 and 6 April 1997, it will be necessary to consider if it may be beneficial for the partners to treat that change as a cessation for tax purposes in order to opt into the new system prematurely.

Cessations before 6 April 1997

Any practice which ceases before 6 April 1997 will be assessed on the existing rules.

Cessation between 6 April 1997 and 5 April 1999

Any business which has been subject to the transitional arrangements in 1996/97 and then ceases prior to 5 April 1998 may be assessed on revised figures for 1995/96 and 1996/97. Effectively the Revenue have the option of applying the existing closing year rules which apply under the preceding year basis whereby the assessments may be revised to actual basis. If a business ceases between 6 April 1998 and 5 April 1999, the Revenue have the right to adjust just 1996/97 to actual.

14 Superannuation

Many GPs only take an interest in their pensions just before they retire. Though understandable, this may be unfortunate because at this late stage the opportunities to change pension arrangements are very limited. Ideally, everyone should be familiar with their pension arrangements and keep them under review.

The NHS pension scheme (NHSPS)

NHS GPs, dentists and ophthalmic practitioners are unique among self-employed practitioners in having an NHS pension. The scheme dates back to the formation of the NHS in 1948 and has remained largely unaltered since then. However, there have been some significant amendments particularly during the last few years, and, at the time of writing, further amendments are being considered.

The NHSPS comprises two quite different schemes; one for independent contractors (principally GPs) and one for salaried employees. The scheme for NHS independent contractors is based on the total of the super-annuable elements of pay (*see* Box 14.1 below) received during the individual's professional career. Because inflation has depressed the value of the income earned in the past, a 'dynamizing' factor has been intro-duced. The other scheme applies to NHS salaried employees (eg hospital doctors) and its benefits are based on the employee's final salary. The reason why GPs are not in a 'final salary' scheme is that their earnings tend to peak earlier in their careers; earnings towards the end are reduced by a decrease in either the volume of work or commitment to the practice, or both.

The NHS GPs' superannuation scheme is certainly unusual and possibly unique. It embodies the concept of a contributory scheme in its purest form in that each and every year's earnings are taken into account when calculating pension entitlement.

Box 14.1: Key features of NHS GPs' superannuation scheme

- superannuable pay in each year of GP service is uprated to take account of subsequent movements in GP earnings (principally due to the effects of inflation) and used as a basis for computing pension entitlements

- standard contribution rate of 6 per cent of superannuable pay

- 45 years of service is maximum permitted contribution base

- salaried trainee service and hospital service can be included in calculation of GP pension, subject to an upper limit of 10 years' service

- GPs can buy 'added years' to increase their pension entitlement

Defining superannuable income

Superannuable income comprises all a GP's earnings as an NHS contractor, from some of which is deducted a notional amount to take account of the expenses element, included in the various fees and allowances. This amount is reviewed and its current value is 35.5 per cent. It is only deducted from certain fees and allowances such as capitation fees, basic practice allowance and item of service fees. Others such as the seniority allowance, training grant and target payments, are treated as being wholly superannuable, and therefore no deduction is made for expenses.

Some sources of income are not superannuable, including direct staff reimbursements, and notional and cost rent payments. A list of fees and allowances showing their superannuable status is in Box 14.2 below.

Box 14.2: The NHS Pension Scheme – superannuable income

Fully superannuable (100 per cent)
- seniority allowance
- training grant
- target payments
- designated area allowance
- inducement payments
- transitional payments
- hospital appointments (clinical assistantships, hospital practitioners, clinics, locums, staff funds)
- course organizer training grant
- GP tutor payments

Partly superannuable (60.3 per cent)
- basic practice allowance
- assistant allowance
- capitation fee
- deprivation payments
- maternity medical service fees
- contraceptive service fees
- temporary resident, immediately necessary treatment, emergency treatment, dental haemorrhage arrest and anaesthetic fees

continued opposite

Box 14.2: *continued*

- night visit fees
- capitation addition for out-of-hours cover
- initial practice allowance
- mileage payments (formerly known as rural practice payments)
- dispensing fees, on-cost oxygen therapy service rents and fees
- drugs and appliances
- postgraduate education allowance
- medical students education allowance
- registration fees
- health promotion payments
- child health surveillance fees
- minor surgery sessional fees
- fees for vaccinations and immunizations carried out for public policy reasons

Non-superannuable

- notional and cost rent allowances
- sickness and maternity payments
- prolonged study leave locum payments
- locum payments for single-handed rural GPs attending courses
- reimbursement for rent and rates, practice staff, computing costs and trainees' salaries
- associate allowance
- fundholding management allowance
- doctors' retainer scheme allowance
- net ingredient cost, container allowance and VAT paid in respect of supply of drugs and appliances
- trainee car allowance and other trainees' expenses
- non-NHS fees:
    - private patients
    - insurance medicals
    - sundry fees: cremations, private certificates, etc.

How contributions are made

Each GP's contributions (currently six per cent of superannuable income) are calculated quarterly by the FHSA or Health Board and shown as a deduction on the quarterly statement. The contributions of GPs in partnerships are calculated by the FHSA or Health Board according to the prevailing profit-sharing ratios. It is important for partnerships to notify the FHSA or Health Board when there is a change in profit-sharing ratios so that this can be reflected in the superannuation deductions. Failure to do so can result in individual partner's pension entitlements being computed incorrectly. If partners are buying added years, the deductions for these should be reflected in their individual drawings.

Tax relief on contributions

The position of GPs is unique in the way in which tax relief is allowed on contributions. Because GPs are not salaried employees there is no statutory entitlement to this relief. The Government has therefore made an extra-statutory concession so that it can be allowed.

A practice's annual accounts should show the contributions of each partner separately in his or her current account, rather than as a deduction in the calculation of partnership profits. This enables partners to benefit from tax relief on contributions being granted on an actual rather than a preceding year basis. Tax relief should therefore be claimed on the GP's personal income tax return and not by including the contributions in the practice accounts or by making a separate claim for personal practice expenses.

Scheme benefits

The benefits available to GPs include:

- an index-linked pension calculated upon 1.4 per cent of the GP's uprated (dynamized) career earnings ('index-linked' means that the pension is increased in April of each year in line with the annual increase in the retail price index (RPI); the actual size of the increase reflects the movement in the RPI during the 12-month period ending the previous September)

- a lump sum payment on retirement entirely free of tax, normally 4.2 per cent of the uprated career earnings (or three times the annual pension). This benefit was not introduced until 1972 but those in practice before then could purchase the equivalent benefit for any preceding years they have been in practice

- widow's pension and (where applicable) widower's pension (applicable to any married doctor with service after 6 April 1988)
- dependent children's benefit payable until the age of 17 years or completion of full-time education
- a death gratuity
- ill health retirement benefit if a GP with two or more years' service has to stop working because of illness.

Opting out of the scheme

Although GPs may opt out of the scheme, almost certainly it would be financially disadvantageous to do so. A few financial services advisers have tried to encourage GPs to leave the scheme at the risk of losing valuable pension rights (including the indexation of pensions) which are virtually impossible to buy in the private sector.

The uprating factor: calculating career earnings

The GP's pension is based on total superannuable earnings throughout his or her career. Government actuaries have calculated that this ensures an equitable arrangement in relation to final year pension schemes. The Health Department keeps a superannuation record for each GP which contains details of superannuable earnings for each year of service. The record shows the monetary value of earnings in each year, which will certainly be at a much lower level during the earlier years as a principal. Because of changes in levels of GP remuneration consequent upon Review Body awards, to match both inflation as well as real pay increases, the earnings recorded for each earlier year are uprated by a factor appropriate to that year to obtain their current value; this process is known as 'uprating' or 'dynamizing'. These uprating factors are updated annually (*see* Box 14.3). All of an individual GP's years' earnings (after uprating) are added together to obtain total superannuable earnings during his or her career. This total figure is used to calculate retirement benefits (*see* Box 14.4).

Box 14.3: Uprating factors applied to GPs' superannuable pay to calculate final pension entitlement

Year ending 31 March	Uprating factor	Year ending 31 March	Uprating factor
1949	24.361	1972	7.832
1950	24.361	1973	7.284
1951	22.536	1974	7.063
1952	22.536	1975	6.460
1953	22.536	1976	4.649
1954	22.536	1977	4.531
1955	22.536	1978	4.361
1956	22.536	1979	3.343
1957	22.424	1980	2.843
1958	20.356	1981	2.395
1959	20.074	1982	2.260
1960	19.192	1983	2.138
1961	18.351	1984	2.002
1962	18.351	1985	1.879
1963	18.351	1986	1.750
1964	16.096	1987	1.646
1965	16.096	1988	1.513
1966	14.634	1989	1.410
1967	13.600	1990	1.306
1968	10.976	1991	1.208
1969	10.758	1992	1.083
1970	10.153	1993	1.015
1971	8.460	1994	1.000

Box 14.3 lists the uprating factors used to calculate GP pensions if they retire on 31 March 1994. GPs can get a copy of their computerized superannuable pay record from the NHS Pensions Agency at:

England & Wales:

NHS Pensions Agency
Hesketh House
200-220 Broadway
Fleetwood, Lancashire
FY7 8LG
Tel: 0253 774774

Northern Ireland:

Health and Personal Social Services
Superannuation Branch (HRD 6)
Waterside House
75 Duke Street
Waterside
Londonderry
BT47 1FP
Tel: 0504 319000

Scotland:

Scottish Office Pensions Agency
St Margaret's House
151 London Road
Edinburgh
EH8 7TG
Tel: 031 244 3585 or 031 556 8400

Box 14.4: Calculating retirement benefits

Dr X practised in the NHS from 1955 and retired on 30 September 1993; he had purchased additional years to bring his total service up to 40 years as well as an unreduced lump sum to cover the years between 1955 and 1972.

Total actual career NHS earnings were £500,000 which, after applying the uprating factors, yielded in this case, uprated career earnings of £1,200,000.

Dr X will receive an annual pension of 1.4 per cent of that amount (£16,800 per annum) and a lump sum of 4.2 per cent of the same amount (£50,400).

Average practitioner service (APS)

This term is widely used in GP pension matters. Its calculation is shown in this example:

Total uprated superannuable remuneration   £1,200,000

Years of practitioner service   30

Average practitioner service $\dfrac{£1,200,000}{30} = £40,000$

APS is used to determine the pension and lump sum value of a GP's previous hospital, community health or war service.

Hospital service

Most GPs have worked in the hospital service, before entering general practice and also subsequently as a clinical assistant or a hospital practitioner. They may also have been paid a salary for some other NHS appointment.

Hospital service and service as a GP trainee prior to becoming a GP principal are treated as 'average practitioner service' (APS), provided its total length is less than 10 years.

The treatment of hospital service after becoming a GP depends upon its length:

• less than the equivalent of one whole time year – the income is added to the GP's superannuable income in the year that it is earned and is dynamized and pensioned in the usual way

• more than one whole time year – the service is assessed separately for pension purposes.

Purchasing extra benefits

The Inland Revenue does not allow total superannuable service to exceed 45 years, and no more than 40 years may be accrued before normal retirement date, that is by age 60. Because most GPs qualify at about age 24, it is not possible for more than 36 years of superannuable service to be acquired by age 60 and GPs are consequently unable to accrue a full pension. The NHSPS therefore allows GPs to purchase additional service in the form of 'added years'.

The added years scheme

The present added years scheme was introduced in the early 1980s. It allows GPs to obtain additional benefits by paying an extra percentage of their NHS superannuable earnings into the scheme; the increased pension and lump sum entitlement compensates for the years of service which could not be counted. There are two limitations:

- total service worked and added years purchased must not exceed 40 years at age 60
- the maximum permitted contribution to the scheme is 15 per cent of superannuable remuneration; because this already includes the standard 6 per cent contributions, the maximum voluntarily additional contribution allowed for added years is 9 per cent. (The 15 per cent is a statutory limitation on the amount allowable for tax relief.)

To younger GPs the cost of buying sufficient added years to establish a full pension entitlement is much less than 9 per cent limit. But for older GPs the effect of the 9 per cent means that they may be unable to purchase all the added years to which they are eligible. As an alternative GPs may opt for added voluntary contributions (AVCs) or free-standing additional voluntary contribution (FSAVCs).

AVCs or FSAVCs

AVCs are 'in-house' arrangements organized by the NHSPS through the Equitable Life Company, whereas FSAVCs may be bought from any life office or other pension company. AVCs/FSAVCs are 'money purchase' schemes, the eventual pension being dependent upon investment returns during the years of contribution and the level of interest (annuity) rates prevailing at retirement. (A 'money purchase' scheme is one in which the pension received ultimately depends on the value of investments purchased from money invested in it, in contrast to a scheme in which the pension reflects final salary and years of service.) They provide extra pension but not a lump sum.

The limit on contributions is the same as applied to added years; thus a GP paying standard contributions at 6 per cent can contribute only another 9 per cent to an AVC/FSAVC scheme. There is a further limitation in that GPs who have already acquired 38 years 1 month of pension entitlement (including any added years) cannot contribute to an FSAVC scheme (for AVCs the limit is 40 years).

Tax relief on AVCs/FSAVCs is allowed by deduction at source; GPs in the higher tax band should obtain additional relief through their normal income tax assessment.

The advantages and disadvantages of AVCs/FSAVCs and added years are set out in Box 14.5 below.

Box 14.5: Added years and AVCs/FSAVCs

Advantages of AVCs/FSAVCs

- greater flexibility because of the option of variable contributions
- added years, once started, are difficult to stop unless extreme financial hardship can be proved
- added years can be prohibitively expensive for older GPs
- tax relief at standard rate obtained at source
- provide a 'mix' of public sector basic benefits and private sector additional benefits

Advantages of added years

- no facility to buy tax-free lump sum with AVCs/FSAVCs
- added years are index-linked
- AVCs/FSAVCs offer no protection for ill-health retirement
- no ancillary benefits unless acquired separately
- the possibility of the AVCs/FSAVCs scheme being overfunded if the benefit is in excess of 66 per cent of final remuneration; this could lead to taxation of the pension fund on retirement
- added years do not depend on investment performance of pension fund

---

The reduced lump sum

Married male GPs working in the NHS before March 1972 receive a lump sum retiring allowance for each year of service prior to that date, at one-third of the rate applicable to each year subsequent to March 1972. However, they may purchase the missing proportion of their lump sum and the arrangements for doing so are similar to the added years scheme.

Contributing to private pension schemes

NHS GPs are uniquely placed in being both self-employed, and members of an occupational pension scheme. This unusual status allows them to contribute to a private pension in respect of:

- non-superannuable income ('topping up')
- superannuable earnings, if existing tax relief on contributions is renounced
- earnings of a spouse employed by the practice.

'Topping-up'

A GP can pay private pension contributions on that proportion of gross relevant earnings (i.e. Schedule D taxable income) derived from non-NHS sources. This is known as 'topping-up' and the amount is calculated by multiplying the standard contributions in any given year by a factor of 100/6; the resulting product is then compared with the Schedule D income. If the Schedule D income is higher, additional contributions can be paid. In practice those GPs with little or no non-NHS income are unlikely to benefit from this arrangement. The calculation should include the GP's Schedule D earnings from all sources, not only from NHS general practice.

Renouncing tax relief

Because the tax relief allowed on GPs' contributions to the NHS pension scheme is concessionary and not statutory, it is only allowed if actually claimed. This arrangement allows a GP to pay pension contributions twice in relation to the same incomes although tax relief can be claimed on only one set of contributions. Although in principle this unique option should be exploited if possible, it will inevitably mean that a GP will incur higher outgoings from his or her disposable income.

A GP's decision to renounce tax relief on NHS contributions continues until revoked. He or she can opt in and out each year, and renunciation can be made for both the current and previous years of assessment, or if there were no relevant earnings in that year, the last but one year of assessment.

15 Fundholding

This chapter outlines the basic principles of the fundholding scheme, which was introduced in 1991 as a key element in the Government's NHS changes. It was designed to give GPs 'buying power' in the new internal market. Although entry was restricted initially to a small minority of practices, it was hoped that their purchasing decisions would serve as a stimulus to the internal market.

What is fundholding?

In summary a fundholding practice:

• negotiates a budget with the Regional Health Authority (RHA) to enable it to purchase a specific range of hospital and community services and to cover the costs of NHS medicines and practice staff

- negotiates contracts with providers for a specific range of hospital care
- has its funds for hospital and community services held by the FHSA, which pays the providers directly on the practice's behalf when authorized to do so by the practice
- has its budget for prescribing costs held on its behalf by the FHSA which is debited for the true NHS cost (i.e. basic price less discount) of medicines prescribed
- receives funds to cover a proportion of staff costs
- can provide a limited range of additional, non-general medical services to its own patients and be paid via the fund
- provides monthly reports and an annual statement of accounts to the FHSA or Health Board
- allows audit of its accounts by the Audit Commission, which should visit the practice at least once every three years
- is allowed to retain any surplus which, after auditing and retention for one year, may be used for health-related projects approved by the RHA
- will be reimbursed up to £17,240 (in 1993/94) for additional expenses actually incurred in preparing to be a fund–holder and up to £34,500 annually for management expenses incurred whilst actually running the fund.

Advantages and disadvantages of fundholding

The following are some advantages.

- Collecting the data can in itself be a useful educational exercise.
- Fundholding enables GPs to plan and manage more directly the care provided for their patients and to make more direct decisions about how NHS money should be spent.
- Fundholders can use savings they make from the fund to improve services for their patients.
- Fundholding allows a more flexible approach to managing the practice.
- Fundholders are able to transfer money from one element of the fund to another.
- The contracting process encourages interaction between NHS bodies which may lead to increased co-operation: for example, close intra-professional relationships between consultants and GPs.

- Fundholders can influence directly how hospital and community health services are delivered to their patients.

Some disadvantages include the following.

- Fundholding entails considerable additional work and responsibility for the practice; in particular the preparatory period involves a significant amount of data collection.
- There is a risk that the doctor/patient relationship could be adversely influenced; a GP could be perceived as the controller of access to health care, instead of the patient's advocate.
- There is a risk of conflict between GPs and hospitals as the NHS internal market becomes increasingly purchase driven. The fundholding practice occupies a position of influence that is unfamiliar to the secondary care sector.
- NHS administrative costs increase, particularly in general practice, but also in hospitals because there are many more purchasers to deal with and substantially more detailed financial and activity reports to provide.
- Fundholding can lead to a two-tier delivery of NHS care.

Applying to become a fundholder

Application and assessment procedures vary, but the following account illustrates how health authorities approach these.

- During September and October (i.e. 18–19 months before fundholding status is to be assumed) FHSAs identify those practices eligible and interested in becoming fundholders and send them the eligibility criteria form. The form requires details of a practice's management arrangements, prescribing policy, computer system and a short statement outlining its reasons for wishing to join the scheme.
- By the end of the following January the FHSA visits applicants and advises the RHA on the suitability of practices.
- By the end of February the RHA approves those practices it considers suitable to commence preparatory work.
- By mid March a plan of how the practice intends to spend the preparatory allowance must be sent to the FHSA.
- By 31 March, the application form for recognition as a fundholding practice must be completed and received by the FHSA. It must be signed by all partners in the practice.

- Data collection takes place between 1 April and 30 September of the preparatory year. These data are based on the discharge letters received by the practice and requests for diagnostic tests and direct access services which it has sent to providers.
- Before fundholding status is confirmed, the practice needs to demonstrate that it has the expertise and management structures to run the fund effectively.
- By the end of December (i.e. three months before 'going live') practices must send their FHSA a purchasing plan which includes a statement of how they satisfy (or propose to satisfy) the assessment criteria and a preliminary plan for the use of the management allowance.
- Successful applicants will be informed by the end of February that they may become fundholders and will receive a budget offer at the same time. A practice must agree the level of fundholding within one month of the offer being made.

The assessment criteria include:

- *list size:* the practice or group of practices must have, or demonstrate that it will have by the start of fundholding, a minimum list size of 7,000 (6,000 in Scotland)
- *partnership commitment:* all partners must be in agreement on entry to fundholding
- *managerial support:* the practice must demonstrate that it will be able to manage the fund effectively, efficiently and economically
- *computing support:* the practice must have the necessary computing hardware and software which complies with Health Department specifications (FHSA grants are available to reimburse costs)
- *data collection:* during the preparatory year practices will have shown that their data collection and analysis is effective
- *purchasing plan:* practices will be asked to produce some form of purchasing plan based on the health needs of their patients within the budgetary constraints.

Preparing for fundholding

Fund management

The fund may be managed by one or more persons, full or part-time. This task may be undertaken by a partner or the practice manager, or the practice may appoint a fund manager. The fund does not have to be managed by an accountant although the practice must have access to accountancy expertise and the partners should be able to understand the accounts.

Staff training

Practice staff will require additional training in various areas, including health needs assessment, negotiating skills and other contracting aspects, computing, business planning, accountancy, financial forecasting and data collection. Part of the preparatory allowance can be used to train staff in skills relevant to fundholding. Computer training costs may be included in software charges and can be claimed from the FHSA as part of the computer reimbursement.

Computing

Prospective fundholders must acquire sufficient computing facilities. There are several suppliers of software whose systems have Health Department approval. The FHSA can advise practices on the choice of software. Fundholders are reimbursed by the FHSA for 100 per cent of the software and associated maintenance and training costs, and 75 per cent of the additional hardware costs, if an approved package is selected and the costs are 'reasonable'. It is advisable to seek the views of other local fundholders about the systems they use.

The preparatory allowance

An allowance is available during the preparatory year. It can be used to employ staff to collate and retrieve data, to train staff, to buy external advice, to pay for locums whilst partners are preparing for fundholding (up to £3,302) and to purchase equipment. (Up to 50 per cent may be spent on equipment.)

Consortia/grouped practices

Grouped practices

Two or more practices each with list sizes below 7,000 may combine to become fundholders. Groups should enter into agreements to apportion the fund, decide how it will be managed and how legal liabilities will be discharged.

Consortia

Practices may form consortia to achieve more negotiating leverage, economies of scale and lower operational costs. This arrangement can enable smaller practices and practices with limited management capacity to participate in the scheme. Each practice/group within a consortium retains responsibility for its budget, even if it is managed centrally.

Scope of the fund

The fund covers four main areas:

- hospital services
- community health services
- prescribed medicines
- practice staff.

Hospital services

The hospital services element covers most outpatient procedures, a defined range of elective inpatient and day case procedures, diagnostic services and direct access services. The fund only covers patients who are registered permanently on the fundholder's list; it excludes temporary residents and includes only those operations and procedures which the Health Department has decided to cover through the fundholding scheme. Therefore, the practice is financially responsible for only those activities that have been initiated or authorized by it, apart from tertiary referrals made by consultants. These must also be paid for from the fund if the practice has been notified of the referral.

The fund does not cover:

- emergency treatment
- obstetrics and genito-urinary medicine
- inpatient stays which do not involve a listed operation or procedure.

There is a £5,000 threshold per patient for hospital and community health services above which the DHA is liable to pay for treatment for the remainder of the financial year. Prescription costs are not included in this threshold.

Community health services

In April 1993 the hospital and community care component was extended to include:

- district nursing
- health visiting
- chiropody
- dietetics
- all community and outpatient mental health services
- mental health counselling
- health services for people with a learning disability
- referrals made by health visitors and district nurses
- referrals made by social services and other agencies to community nursing services and to learning disabilities services.

Prescribing costs

The fund covers all prescribing on FP10s including drugs and appliances; the £5,000 limit does not apply to the prescribing budget.

Practice staff costs

There is no formal guidance to cover the use of the practice staff element of the fund over and above the requirements of the terms of service and statement of fees and allowances. Fundholders must ensure that quality of care to patients is maintained and staff must be appropriately qualified and experienced.

The management allowance

Because managing the fund is an additional task for the practice, fundholders are entitled to a management allowance of up to £34,500 (for 1993/94). This can be used in various ways:

- paying wages to manage the fund
- paying for accountancy, consultancy or other professional services
- purchase of equipment (e.g. computers) – up to 25 per cent of the allowance.

Contracts

There are four basic types of contract.

Block contracts

This is the simplest type: the practice pays an annual fee in instalments to a hospital for access to a specific range of services; for example, pathology or radiography services. This contract may be viewed as funding a given level of activity (known as an indicative volume). At practice level costs must still be attributed (albeit notionally) to individual patients.

Cost and volume contracts

Hospitals receive a sum for a baseline level of activity defined in terms of a predetermined number of treatments or cases; beyond this level funding is on a cost per case basis.

Cost per case contracts

The payment is on a case by case basis, without prior commitment to the volume of cases which might be referred.

Fixed price non attributable contracts

The contract is fixed price in that it is not sensitive in any way to volume or activity. No referrals are recorded in the fundholding software and therefore costs and referrals are not attributable to individual patients. (This means that the £5,000 limit per patient cannot apply.) This differs from a block contract where notional costs are always attributed to individual patients. In 1993/94 this type has been extended to apply to community services.

Contracting with non-NHS providers

Fundholders may contract with private providers of specialist services if they have been allocated a provider number by the RHA. Fundholders should ensure that the professional staff providing care are properly qualified. Fundholders should note that contracts with non-NHS bodies are legally binding on the practice. (In 1993/94 community staff contracts may only be made with current NHS providers.)

Special referral arrangements

Practices may arrange with NHS providers for consultants to hold NHS sessions in their surgery premises. Alternatively, fundholders may employ directly the services of a consultant (or another practitioner such as a physiotherapist) on a private basis if this is less costly, or perhaps more convenient, than an outpatient referral to an NHS hospital. Such practitioners could be employed on the practice premises or elsewhere. In these circumstances, as with GPs acting in a private capacity, the patient remains an NHS patient but the consultant or practitioner is working in a private capacity and cannot count this work as an NHS session.

The extension of services provided by fundholders

Since April 1993 fundholders have been able to offer a limited range of services (e.g. vasectomies, varicose vein surgery, blood counts, upper gastrointestinal endoscopy, colposcopy and audiometry) covered by the scheme to their own patients, over and above those services provided within general medical services, and may make an appropriate charge on the fund for these. These new arrangements bar limited companies from being used by fundholders to provide services to patients.

Managing the fund

It is the responsibility of the fundholder to ensure that the fund allocated to them is managed 'efficiently and effectively'.

Overspending

The RHA receives an overall cash limited financial allocation for all purchasers in its region; therefore a fundholder's fund is acquired at the expense of DHA purchasers because they no longer have to purchase those services covered by the fund on behalf of fundholders' patients.

An overspend resulting from poor management may lead to a practice losing its fundholding status. Where overspends occur, additional funding has to be provided by RHAs to meet the fundholder's commitments so that services to patients are not interrupted. In some circumstances an RHA may consider that an overspend is due to factors outside the control of the fundholder and not therefore due to mismanagement; for example, if the overspend is caused by:

- an unanticipated significant increase in list size
- an unanticipated significant increase in the number of high cost patients on the practice list (especially if they need high cost drugs)
- a serious epidemic
- errors or discrepancies in either the data or the costs used by the RHA as the basis for setting the level of the fund.

The 1993 regulations include powers to enable RHAs to recover misapplied sums through the civil courts. The Health Department has assured the BMA that it has no intention of using the 'misapplication' regulation to initiate proceedings against any fundholding practice which *inadvertently* overspends on its funds on activities covered by NHS Acts.

Underspending and use of savings

Underspending may be due to various circumstances:

- fundholders may make savings in a particular area: for example, they may adopt a new prescribing policy and make savings on this component of the fund
- fundholders may obtain unplanned savings: for example, they expect (and plan for) a higher level of service than their patients actually require
- the original level of the fund from the RHA may have been inaccurate.

If the underspending is due to the RHA setting the level of the fund too high, the fundholder is permitted to keep the unspent money as savings. However, the level will obviously be reviewed in subsequent years. Fundholders cannot spend savings until they have been officially audited. They may be carried over for up to four years. Savings can be spent on activities covered by the fund, or for one or more of the following purposes (subject to RHA approval):

- purchasing materials or equipment which:
  - can be used for the treatment of patients in the practice
  - enhance the comfort or convenience of patients
  - enable the practice to be managed more effectively and efficiently

- purchasing of materials or equipment relating to health education
- improving the practice premises or its furnishings and fitting.

Fundholders will only be able to fund practice staff posts for the period it takes to use up the sum allocated from the savings; therefore staff may have to be appointed on a temporary basis.

The RHA is responsible for ensuring the fundholders' proposed use of savings comply with the fundholding regulations.

16 Medical Politics: How GPs are Represented

LIKE their counterparts in other branches of the medical profession, GPs belong to a wide variety of representational, professional and learned bodies, and pressure groups. Some cater for the entire profession such as the General Medical Council, BMA, the medical defence organizations and the Royal Society of Medicine; whereas others serve the interests of a minority, for example the Overseas Doctors Association, Dispensing Doctors Association and the National Association of Fundholding Practices. This chapter explains how the interests of all GPs are collectively represented through their own democratic machinery, which is based on the links between LMCs and the BMA's GMSC.

Because it is such a well-established profession, medicine enjoys a large measure of self government in its relationship to the State. This self government has generated a variety of medico-political institutions, including those which enable doctors to be represented on bodies concerned with running of the NHS. In particular, NHS GPs are represented by a national body, the GMSC, and a network of 117 LMCs.

Background

The origins of the GMSC and the LMCs date back to 1913, when a publicly funded health service (albeit restricted to providing GP services to a minority of the adult population) was first introduced by Lloyd George's National Insurance Act. When this legislation was proposed it made no provision for GPs to be involved in the running of the new state health service. However, the BMA was determined that the profession should have a voice and its efforts ensured that locally elected committees of GPs (LMCs) were statutorily recognized in the Act as the democratic voice of GPs in each locality. Thus the Act required Local Insurance Committees

(the forerunners of NHS Executive Councils, Family Practitioner Committees (FPCs) and latterly FHSAs), whose task was to run this new health
insurance scheme, to consult through the LMC all GPs participating in the
new health service on many administrative and professional matters.

Once LMCs were established, the BMA formed a national committee
based on them to represent GPs' interests in negotiations with government. This committee, the Insurance Acts Committee, the forerunner of
the GMSC, was recognized by government as the democratic voice of GPs.

The Liberal Government agreed to these arrangements for representing
GPs because the success of its health insurance scheme depended on the
willing co-operation of GPs. Although the profession ostensibly supported
the concept of a state medical scheme it was opposed to it being provided
by salaried doctors. It recognized that if GPs' independent contractor
status was replaced by a salaried service this would undermine their freedom to practice without state interference and affect adversely patient
care. GPs and their representatives rightly suspected that government
would attempt to influence their day-to-day care of patients.

The overriding commitment to the independent contractor status remains a guiding principle of the GMSC. Had it not been for the tenacity
of its forerunner (the Insurance Acts Committee) on this crucial issue, GPs
could have been sucked into a salaried service (as were their hospital
colleagues in 1948). The well-tested and proven value of the contract for
service with local insurance committees led to this type of contract continuing and developing within the NHS following its inception in 1948.
The Local Insurance Committees recognized that this contract worked
well and sought successfully to preserve it in the new NHS structure.

FHSAs recognize LMCs

LMCs must be formally recognized by FHSAs in order to carry out their
statutory functions and raise funds through the statutory levy for their
day-to-day operation. This statutory recognition of the LMC has parallels
elsewhere in the public sector; legislation enacted in the 1940s to nation-
alize public utilities and major industries explicitly recognized trade
unions and professional associations for negotiating and consultative purposes. The statutory recognition accorded to LMCs was granted almost
40 years earlier; the earliest example in the UK of an organization being
recognized by statute to represent those providing a publicly funded
service.

Three types of functions and duties of LMCs derive from their recognition by FHSAs:

- those based on the 'partnership principle' (originating in 1911): on many key issues LMCs and FHSAs determine jointly what policies and actions should be implemented. This local recognition and representation ensures the efficient provision of general medical services, enabling FHSAs to draw upon the goodwill and experience of local GPs. The process of consultation also ensures that the terms of service (negotiated centrally by the GMSC and Health Department) are fairly and reasonably applied locally

- those concerned with administering the GP contract. FHSAs are obliged to consult LMCs on many issues; this is evident in the regulations governing NHS general medical services, GPs' terms of service and the statement of fees and allowances. The LMC also plays an important role in both the complaints procedure and the investigation of certain matters relating to professional conduct

- those concerned with representing GPs as a whole.

In many ways the partnership principle has been discarded and replaced by the managerial ethos associated with the 1990 GP contract. Formerly, successive governments had recognized the value of special arrangements for administering GP contracts which took account of their independent contractor status. Before the 1990 contract, eight of the 30 FPC members were LMC nominees. Now only one member of the much smaller FHSA 'executive' is a GP, whose appointment is at the discretion of the RHA. FHSAs will soon be merged with District Health Authorities; it is reasonable to assume that those relationships should continue unchanged in the new unified authority.

LMCs also provide many other services for their GP constituents which vary according to local 'custom and practice'. These include handling local ethical problems, representing GPs in relations with bodies and organizations outside the NHS, and promoting the standing of general practice both in the media and among the public generally. To this end many LMCs have established close ties with MPs, local councillors, community health councils, and other professions such as nursing, health visiting and social work.

Other health service bodies

The LMC also serves as a point of reference for other NHS bodies seeking GPs' views; a perusal of LMC activities shows that this is a large part of their work. Although GPs are no longer represented, as of right, on RHAs or DHAs, a few continue to serve on these bodies. In some areas, LMCs appoint doctors to serve on regional medical advisory committees, regional GP advisory subcommittees, purchasing advisory bodies, district medical advisory committees (where these are established), and also on variously named district medical liaison/executive committees, the regional GP subcommittees for postgraduate medical education, and many other *ad hoc* committees and working groups (clinical and administrative) at regional, district and local levels. LMCs are consulted when GPs are appointed to many offices and posts, and they play an active part in advising their local health authorities on a range of policy matters, including recently, and most importantly, the commissioning of secondary care. In short, LMCs have a continuing dialogue with other parts of the NHS. They also become involved in many other issues affecting GPs locally: examples include clinical assistant and hospital practitioner grade posts, GP hospitals and units, GP beds, and access to diagnostic facilities.

LMCs medico-political functions

The LMC is an independent self-financing body with statutory functions (as distinct from a state-funded statutory body). Its independent status allows it to exercise medico-political and statutory functions. This duality of roles is unique and contributes to its strength. The statutory functions are mostly concerned with protecting the interests of individual GPs in relation to their contract with the FHSA, and also with the continuing consultations and negotiations between LMCs and FHSAs. On the other hand, the medico-political functions are concerned primarily with the collective interests of GPs as a group, and they operate through a quite separate channel consisting of the annual conference of LMC representatives and the GMSC.

In some areas, regional committees of LMCs provide a forum for discussing supra-district problems and exchanging ideas and experience. Since the FPCs were reconstituted as FHSAs under the control of RHAs, many LMCs have understandably sought to act collectively via a regional LMC committee to formulate policy and co-ordinate activities at regional level. The Health Department has delegated to RHAs responsibility for resolving most of the day-to-day problems raised by FHSAs. In these circumstances regional LMCs committees are becoming an important link with RHAs. However, the Functions and Manpower Review published by the Department of Health in 1993 envisages major changes in the functions and organization of the intermediate tier of the NHS (currently the RHA), and these changes could have considerable repercussions on professional representation at regional level.

GMSC

The GMSC is a BMA committee with authority to deal with all matters affecting NHS GPs. It represents all GPs in Great Britain, whether or not they are members of the BMA (in fact some 80 per cent are members).

The committee is recognized as the sole negotiating body for general practice by the Health Department and is represented in negotiations with ministers and civil servants by a team of five GPs who draw upon their day-to-day experience of general practice and are assisted by full-time expert advisers. The team is supplemented by other GMSC members and legal, accountancy and other specialist advice as and when necessary.

The GMSC has 83 members, of whom 44 are directly elected representatives of LMCs. It meets monthly and much of its work is done by subcommittees (see Box 16.1). It is represented on most national bodies concerned with health, providing an essential medical input which is firmly rooted in the day-to-day experience of general practice (see Box 16.2). The Welsh and Scottish GMSCs are subcommittees of the national GMSC, but have autonomy on NHS matters exclusive to their countries. The Northern Ireland GMSC is autonomous of the GMSC but it has close working relations with it.

Box 16.1: The GMSC subcommittees' activities

Scottish GMSC

- GPs working in the NHS in Scotland: negotiates directly with the Scottish Home and Health Department

Welsh GMSC

- GPs working in the NHS in Wales: negotiates directly with the Welsh Office

General purposes subcommittee

- all matters referred to it by the GMSC; also considers relationships between GPs and colleagues in other health professions

Educational and audit subcommittee

- all matters relating to professional audit, vocational training, undergraduate and continuing education for GPs

Computing subcommittee

- the development and application of computers in general practice

Commissioning of care subcommittee

- advises on how to involve GPs in the commissioning process

Fundholding subcommittee

- represents the interests of fundholding GPs

Hospital and special services subcommittee

- terms of service and contractual arrangements of GPs working in hospitals: obstetric care, minor surgery, child health surveillance, contraceptive services, cervical cytology and health promotion

Prescribing subcommittee

- prescribing and the supply of medicines

Practice organization subcommittee

- practice organization, including staff employment, practice equipment and patient record systems

Practice premises subcommittee

- practice premises, including the direct reimbursement scheme, leases, structural modifications and improvement and design of surgeries

Rural practice subcommittee

- general practice in rural areas, including GP dispensing

Statute and regulations subcommittee

- any NHS Acts, statutory instruments and other parliamentary legislation relevant to NHS general practice

Trainees subcommittee

- represents the interests of GP vocational trainees

Box 16.2: GMSC representation on outside bodies

Advisory Committee on Borderline Substances
Advisory Committee on NHS drugs
Association of Medical Secretaries, Practice Administrators
    and Receptionists

Chief Executive/Chief Medical Officers Working Group
Chief Executive Working Group on Information
    Management and Technology
Child Health Computing Committee
  • child health data subcommittee
  • systems information and development subcommittee
  • steering committee
Churches Council for Health and Healing
Clinical Standards Advisory Group
Committee on Standards of Data Extraction
Computer Research and Development Committee
Confidential Enquiry into Genetic Disorders

English National Board for Nursing, Midwifery and
    Health Visiting

Family Planning Association, Medical Advisory Committee

General Dental Services Committee
General Optical Council
General Practice Finance Corporation

Health Services Information Steering Group
Health Visitors Education and Training Council

Inducement Payments Committee
Initial Practice Allowance Committee

Joint Committee for Continuing Education of Practice Staff
Joint Committee on Postgraduate Training for
    General Practice

Joint Committee on Vaccination and Immunisation
Joint Computing Group
Joint Formulary Committee

Maternity Allowance
Medical Practices Committee

continued opposite

Box 16.2: *continued*

Medical Whitley Council – Committee A – staff side (functional)

Misuse of Drugs Act 1971 – professional panels and tribunals

National Cervical Screening Programme Coordinating Network

NHS Centre for Coding and Classification Supervisory Board

NHS Tribunal

Prescribers' Journal committee of management

Prescription Pricing Authority

Public Health Medicine Consultative Committee

Registrar General's medical advisory committee

Royal College of General Practitioners
- council
- education committee
- liaison committee
- postgraduate training committee

Royal College of Surgeons – council

Rural Practices Fund – central advisory committee

Service Committees and Tribunal Regulations
- medical advisory committees
- disciplinary enquiries

Standing Committee on Postgraduate Medical Education

Standing Medical Advisory Committee (DoH)

Trainer Appeals Committees

Union of European GPs (UEMO)

The GMSCs policy-making procedures operate on an annual cycle. It sends all GPs an annual report of its work in March. Individual GPs can influence policy through their LMCs which consider the report and submit its motions to the annual conference of LMC representatives which is held in June. This conference, comprising more than 300 GPs appointed by LMCs, is the professions principal policy-making body. Those motions which are approved by the conference are referred to the GMSC to implement. This democratic process gives credibility to the GMSC's day-to-day activities as the representative voice of all NHS GPs.

This description of the LMCs conference/GMSC structure shows how GPs have exercised 'self-government' through their LMCs. Every part of the UK has at least one spokesperson on the GMSC; a doctor working in practice who can represent its problems and express its views on issues affecting negotiations for GPs as a whole.

Negotiations with government

There is a regular cycle of meetings between the GMSC negotiating team and a team of Health Department officials, and these are supplemented by many other meetings to deal with specific matters. Indeed, contact between the GMSC secretariat and the Health Department is normally as frequent as several times each working day; thus there is a continuing dialogue between the two sides. Over the years negotiations have covered a wide range of issues. In practice, the satisfactory completion of negotiations only occasionally results in major amendments to the Red Book and, even more rarely, amendments to the legal framework of general practice, the NHS regulations (which include the GP's terms of service). It is important to note that the Red Book, although technically part of the NHS regulations, can be amended without parliamentary approval, whereas because the NHS regulations themselves are parliamentary enactments they require parliamentary approval to amend their provisions.

The imposition of the 1990 contract

The imposition of new contractual arrangements, together with other managerial changes emanating from the Government's White Paper *Working for Patients*, created a very different climate of relations between the GMSC and the Health Department, and between LMCs and FHSAs.

In 1990, after many months of negotiations, the Government imposed a new contract on an unwilling and hostile profession. In doing so it was determined that 'negotiations' with the profession did not imply having to reach an agreement with it; thereby consciously abandoning a long tradition (extending back to the beginnings of the family doctor service in 1913) of proceeding by consensus and introducing contract changes only after agreement with representatives of the profession.

However, during the past four years, relations at national level between the profession's representatives and ministers and their officials have steadily returned to normality and successful negotiations have been achieved in several areas.

At local level, relations between LMCs and FHSAs are undergoing a far more permanent and fundamental change. Implementation of the NHS reforms has involved a major revision of structure, management and line of accountability of FHSAs, and the old principle of partnership with LMCs has virtually disappeared.

General medical services defence fund

This representative system involves a considerable expenditure of time and money, and the Defence Fund (first established in 1913) is the main source of funds for running it. The term 'defence' may appear to be a misnomer if narrowly defined to apply only to some form of direct action against Government (eg the collection of undated resignations from the NHS); however, the GMSC's work together with that of its subcommittees and working groups, is aimed at defending GPs' interests both collectively and individually, even though the profession may not be engaged in a confrontation with Government on any specific issue. All this activity costs money; it could be described as the price the profession has to pay for 'self-government'.

Statutory and voluntary levies

Most of the income for the defence fund comes from voluntary contributions raised by LMCs from their constituent GPs. This voluntary levy is quite distinct from the statutory levy; the latter may be used only 'for defraying the administrative expenses of the LMC, including travelling and subsistence allowances payable to its members'. Although the legislation allows LMCs (in England and Wales only) to make a compulsory statutory levy on every GP to meet these specific expenses, not all LMCs choose to do so. Each LMC determines for itself whether to raise its funds from either the voluntary levy or both the voluntary and statutory levies.

17 Entering General Practice: The GP Vocational Training Scheme

Before 1981, when vocational training for general practice became mandatory, any fully registered medical practitioner could apply to fill a GP vacancy as a partner or single-handed practitioner. However, a doctor without previous GP experience was rarely admitted to an FPC medical list. Long before vocational training became compulsory, most doctors wishing to become GPs were already extending their obligatory one year pre-registration hospital training by gaining further hospital experience, as well as filling traineeships, or sometimes assistantships, before joining a practice.

The vocational training regulations

These regulations govern entry to general practice; all doctors applying to become NHS GP principals, whether single-handed or in partnership, have to show that they have acquired a specified range of postgraduate experience. Currently they do not apply to doctors who work as:

- whole-time practitioners in private general practice
- assistants in NHS general practice
- restricted services principals in the NHS; that is providing services which are limited to child health surveillance, contraceptive services, maternity medical services, minor surgery services, or some combination of these
- deputies for commercial deputizing services.

Other doctors may be exempt because:

- they were already GP principals on 15 February 1981 when the regulations first applied (these doctors remain permanently exempt and if they resign and subsequently return to general practice this exemption is preserved)
- they have been engaged on comparable duties in the armed forces to those of general practice.

The regulations prescribe what clinical experience has to be acquired to obtain the 'certificate of prescribed experience' issued by the Joint Committee on Postgraduate Training for General Practice (JCPTGP). The Medical Practices Committee (MRC) which ultimately determines whether a vacancy (in a partnership or single-handed) should be filled, and who should fill it, requires all applications for a principalship to be supported by a JCPTGP certificate.

Because the UK is required to implement a European directive on GP vocational training it is now proposed that all doctors working in general practice should be required to satisfy the vocational training regulations. At the time of writing it is not clear whether exemption will be allowed for those doctors with previous experience of general practice in posts other than principal posts.

What is 'prescribed experience'?

This requires three years' training comprising:

- at least one year as a trainee GP
- at least one year comprising two or more hospital appointments of at least six months each in two or more of these specialties: accident and

emergency medicine or general surgery, general medicine, geriatrics, obstetrics and/or gynaecology, paediatrics, psychiatry. The entire hospital 'leg' of the vocational training may be confined to any two of these specialties

- alternatively any remaining period (up to one year) may be spent on one or more of a wider range of hospital or community medicine posts or in a GP training practice.

These posts must be 'educationally approved' which means being approved by the Royal College or Faculty relevant to each specialty, and being selected by a regional postgraduate education committee as suitable for GP vocational training.

GP trainers (i.e. the approval of GP training posts) are selected by regional committees for postgraduate medical education, advised by their general practice subcommittees.

Vocational trainees have to obtain a 'statement of satisfactory completion' for each separate appointment they have filled and present these to the JCPTGP.

Box 17.1:

'Satisfactory completion' of a period of training is defined as completing it "in such a manner as to have acquired the medical experience which may reasonably be expected from training of that duration in that employment".

The formal definition of 'satisfactory completion' in Box 17.1 makes no reference to any requirement that GP trainees should demonstrate the knowledge and skills they have acquired. However, legal advice has confirmed that satisfactory completion indicates a satisfactory level of competence, according to the assessment of the person signing the statement of satisfactory completion, and this view has been jointly endorsed by the chairmen of the GMSC, the JCPTGP and the Council of the RCGP. Thus doctors completing vocational training for general practice are expected to have achieved a satisfactory standard of competence and performance, and the JCPTGP is currently proposing that regions should implement a process of summative assessment to guarantee that an appropriate standard has been achieved.

Equivalent experience

Other kinds of clinical experience which do not necessarily fulfil the criteria of prescribed experience may count as 'equivalent' to prescribed experience; examples include:

- posts occupied on a less than half-time basis or for less than six months
- experience gained outside the UK
- 'electives'
- experience gained in occupational health.

If the JCPTGP is satisfied that a doctor's overall experience is indeed equivalent to that prescribed by the regulations it issues a certificate of equivalent experience, which has the same standing as a 'prescribed' experience certificate.

Equivalent experience provides a way of satisfying the regulations other than by conventional vocational training. However, the experience gained must equate in educational terms with that prescribed in the regulations; the standardized programme of training and its permitted variations. The difficulties of equating like with like are considerable and the JCPTGP has developed a substantial body of case law which enables it to judge whether a particular range of experience satisfies the criteria. A doctor has a right to appeal to the Secretary of State against the JCPTGP's refusal to issue a certificate of prescribed or equivalent experience.

Vocational training schemes

Normally, full vocational training involves a three-year structured scheme which is usually undertaken immediately after GMC registration. Two of these three years are normally spent in Senior House Officer (SHO) posts and the other in a training practice.

Most GP trainees do their training within a three-year structured scheme organized by regional postgraduate medical education committees. The structured scheme provides a series of rotations in hospital posts and a training practice or practices. Its main advantage is that trainees do not have to find and apply for a succession of posts; they therefore enjoy a greater security of tenure and can plan their lives around the three years of training. The posts on the rotation will be approved educationally and there should be fewer problems in obtaining time off to attend weekly day or half-day release courses.

The other alternative is the self-constructed training programme which can offer greater flexibility in the type and location of hospital posts. This arrangement may be particularly beneficial for doctors who are undecided about their careers and want to keep their options open. The main disadvantage is that they have to compete for a series of posts.

Part-time training

The vocational training regulations allow part-time employment in approved training posts to qualify as prescribed experience, provided the overall length of training is extended proportionately. Part-time is not restricted to half-time employment; less than half-time training may be aggregated to count towards equivalent experience.

A model contract for GP trainees

The details of a GP trainee's employment contract are not governed by the vocational training regulations, which pay no regard to hours of duty and holiday arrangements. These and other matters should be agreed before the traineeship in general practice starts and encapsulated in a written employment contract. A model contract is available to BMA members from their local office. However, the trainee's salary and a range of specific allowances and direct reimbursements (particularly those relating to removal expenses) are specified in the Red Book (*see* Box 17.2) and the

---

Box 17.2: GP trainees' allowances and direct reimbursement

- removal and relocation expenses: these are extensive and complex and based on the NHS General Whitley Council conditions of service
- travelling expenses
- interview expenses
- payment during sickness
- maternity leave payments
- expenses for postgraduate examinations

Full details of all these payments are in paragraph 38 of the Red Book.

---

trainer does not exercise any discretion in relation to these payment. The trainee's salary is fixed by reference to his or her other previous hospital posts. Thus the salary is therefore substantially higher for a former registrar than for someone who was previously an SHO. A trainer cannot pay a trainee more than the appropriate salary specified in the Red Book.

Payments made to the GP trainer

The following are paid to trainers when they employ trainees:

- a training grant (an allowance for the additional work and costs incurred by employing a trainee)
- reimbursement of the employer's share of the trainee's NI contributions (the trainee pays the employee's share)
- a car or motor vehicle allowance, if the practice needs an additional vehicle for the trainee
- the cost of installing an extra telephone at the surgery and a telephone at the trainee's residence
- the rental charge for a telephone at the trainee's residence (provided the trainee is responsible for paying it) and the cost of installation and rental charge for a bedroom telephone extension at the trainee's home, if both the FHSA and trainer are satisfied that it is necessary
- the trainee's salary which is related to the basic salary in the previous NHS hospital post
- reimbursement of the trainee's medical defence organization subscription or premium costs, less any costs which would have been incurred if they had taken out the basic subscription ('additional cover') payable by hospital doctors. The trainer must have evidence of the trainee's subscription or premium being paid. The reimbursement may be paid in one lump sum or in monthly instalments to reflect the trainee's arrangements for paying the subscription and length of service with the trainer.

The trainer is responsible for administering the trainee's NIC and PAYE.

Appendix 1: Local BMA Offices and Staff

THE BMA has 17 local offices throughout the UK. There are 12 offices in England, reflecting the RHAs; and offices in Scotland, Wales and Northern Ireland.

England

The BMA's local offices in England are divided between the Northern Province and the Southern Province, each with its own Provincial Secretary.

Northern Province

Mersey
(includes Isle of Man)

22 Oxford Street
Liverpool. L7 7BL
Tel: 051 709 5660
Fax: 051 709 5376

North East

Old Brewery Court
Sandyford Road
Jesmond
Newcastle. NE2 1XG
Tel: 091 261 7131
Fax: 091 261 6203

North West

Bartree House
460 Palatine Road
Northenden
Manchester. M22 4DJ
Tel: 061 945 8989
Fax: 061 945 5045

Trent

301 Glossop Road
Sheffield. S10 2HL
Tel: 0742 721705
Fax: 0742 751686

West Midlands

36 Harborne Road
Edgbaston
Birmingham. B15 3AJ
Tel: 021 456 1402
Fax: 021 456 3439

Yorkshire

Sterling House
Northside Business Park
Sheepscar
Leeds. LS7 2BB
Tel: 0532 458745
Fax: 0532 421867

Southern Province

Cambridge

10 Downing Street
Cambridge. CB2 3DS
Tel: 0223 64539
Fax: 0223 464743

North Thames

BMA House
Tavistock Square
London. WC1H 9JP
Tel: 071 383 8296
Fax: 071 383 6911

Oxford

Cranbrook House
287 Banbury Road
Summertown
Oxford. OX2 7JF
Tel: 0865 59621
Fax: 0865 58082

South Thames

Venture House
15 High Street
Purley
Surrey. CR8 2XA
Tel: 081 660 5558
Fax: 081 668 0117

Bristol	4th Floor Centre Gate Colston Avenue Bristol. BS1 4TR Tel: 0272 227645 Fax: 0272 252494
Winchester (includes Channel Islands)	Star Lane House Staple Gardens Winchester. SO23 8SR Tel: 0962 856760 Fax: 0962 856761

Scotland

South East Scotland	3 Hill Place Edinburgh. EH8 9EQ Tel: 031 662 4820 Fax: 031 667 6933
West of Scotland	2 Woodside Place Glasgow. G3 7QF Tel: 041 332 1862 Fax: 041 332 2259
North of Scotland	11 Pinkie Road Newmachar Aberdeenshire AB2 0RG Tel/Fax: 0651 862004

Wales

	1 Cleeve House Cardiff Business Park Llanishen Cardiff. CF4 5GJ Tel: 0222 766277 Fax: 0222 766162

Northern Ireland

61 Malone Road
Belfast. BT9 6SA
Tel: 0232 663272
Fax: 0232 666318

Index